Doctor in the Soup

By the same author

NOVELS

Doctor in the House
Doctor at Sea
Doctor at Large
Doctor in Love
Doctor and Son
Doctor in Clover
Doctor on Toast
Doctor in the Swim
Doctor on the Boil
Doctor on the Brain
Doctor in the Nude
Doctor on the Job
Doctor in the Nest
Doctors' Daughters
The Captain's Table
Doctor on the Ball

Nuts in May
The Summer of Sir Lancelot
Love and Sir Lancelot
The Facemaker
Surgeon at Arms
The Facts of Life
The Medical Witness
The Sleep of Life
The Invisible Victory
The Private Life of
   Florence Nightingale
The Private Life of
   Jack the Ripper
The Private Life of Dr
   Crippen

GENERAL

Good Neighbours
Happy Families
Instant Fishing
Fifty years a Fisherman

Bedside Manners
Dr Gordon's Casebook
Great Medical Disasters
Great Medical Mysteries

BY MARY AND RICHARD GORDON
A Baby in the House

Doctor in the Soup

Richard Gordon

Century
London Melbourne Auckland Johannesburg

First published in Great Britain in 1986 by
Century Hutchinson Ltd, Brookmount House,
62–65 Chandos Place, Covent Garden, London WC2N 4NW

Century Hutchinson Publishing Group (Australia) Pty Ltd
16–22 Church Street, Hawthorn, Melbourne, Victoria 3122

Century Hutchinson (NZ) Ltd
32–34 View Road, PO Box 40–086, Glenfield, Auckland 10

Century Hutchinson Group (SA) Pty Ltd
PO Box 337, Bergvlei 2012, South Africa

Set in Linotron 202 Baskerville by Inforum Ltd, Portsmouth
Printed and bound in Great Britain by
Anchor Brendon Limited, Tiptree, Essex

British Library Cataloguing in Publication Data
Gordon, Richard, *1921–*
Doctor in the soup.
I. Title

ISBN 0–7126–9481–1

In the beginning Nye created the National Health Service on 5 July 1948 (a Monday).

And its genesis was a hotchpotch of workhouses, drains, dispensaries, asylums, infirmaries, friendly societies, flag days, visions, traditions, pities, prejudices and quirks, the chaotic bequest of Victorian benevolence.

And Nye created great whales of hospital consultants and creeping things of GPs like me.

And Nye saw that it was good.

And Nye's creatures were faithful and multiplied, and now cost his countrymen thirteen billion quid a year.

And the National Health Service came to enjoy the same cloying affection of the British public as the Royal Family.

What Nye Bevan preached I practise in Churchford, an admirably complacent old Kent market town, peopled by commuters unduly concerned with over-indulgence in calories and under-indulgence in sex. Nye's gospel was of free treatment for the sickly masses making everyone so healthy that the medical profession would shortly wither away. Engels had the same touching optimism about the State under the spreading benefits of communism

Doctors' fingermarks lie thicker on our lives because the national health has changed more spectacularly than the National Health Service, which after thirty years was reorganized so thoroughly that five years later it needed reorganizing all over again.

The dead are now the elderly. The fiery illnesses which crisped young lives are quenched, the smouldering ones of age dismally commonplace. Psychology throws deeper shadows, as deceitfully as moonshine. Everyone wants to confide everything in the doctor, because in the age of mass communications nobody communicates with anyone. Patients demand medical miracles, as advertised by the newspapers. The whole country gets depressed, particularly in November.

The doctor's art meanwhile remains age-old. He mixes high intelligence with low cunning, saintliness with bawdiness, and barters intimidation of his patients for idolization of himself. Even from a cocksure, snook-cocking world, his vocation exacts the esteem of no other.

I am proud of my son Andy, on a year's cardiac research at Johns Hopkins Hospital in Baltimore, and of my daughter Jilly, enjoying the dawning rays of surgical glory as a registrar at the Churchford General.

I am fond of my wife Sandra, who remains amazingly resilient to the ravages of pregnancy, the menopause and marriage to myself. Though her hair is devalued from gold to silver, I sometimes see her as the St Swithin's staff nurse I wed. This is possibly because I never have my glasses on in our intimate moments. Myopia maintains many marriages.

I contentedly wear the unadorned social label, 'a good sort'. I work with three agreeable partners in a custom-built surgery squatting amid the seedy semis surrounding the station, overtopped by the supermarket and multistorey car park, the cathedrals and castles of our age.

I live where I first underpinned the NHS single-handed, among quiet avenues aforested with laburnum, cherry and rowan, in a genial red-brick, slate-roofed Victorian villa masked by laurel and box, where one bright April morning I went downstairs as usual in my pyjamas to gather the Sunday papers from our rustic porch.

Horror!

My life was in ruins.

2

Two Friday evenings earlier, our popular local MP young Jim Whynn had telephoned for a consultation.

I was leaving the surgery off Chaucer Way for home in Foxglove Lane, but drove at once to the converted oast house where newly-married Jim had arrived two winters before to nurse the constituency.

The following spring, Sandra and I were startled by an invitation to dinner.

'He's working his way through the local notables,' she decided dampingly. 'There'll be a dozen there, including that awful launderette millionaire you got blackballed at the golf club.'

I countered, 'But it would be like turning down an invitation to a Palace garden party.'

She was suddenly interested. 'Might he wangle us an invitation? I'd love seeing what's behind at Buckingham Palace, quite as fascinating as looking into another woman's kitchen.'

The oast house still sparkled with fresh paint. A foreign girl in a pretty overall opened the door, another smilingly took Sandra's wrap. The sitting room was circular and white-walled, the pictures dignified, the furniture beautifully polished and arranged. It was like being stood a drink in an antique dealer's.

Beside the brick hearth with fire-dogs stood Jim, tall, fair, smooth-skinned, handsome, conscientiously charming. His wife Charlotte on the chintz sofa was dark, articulate, solicitous and lovely. It rosily dawned we were the only guests. I winked at Sandra over the new round bifocals which my more bookish patients say encourage my diverting resemblance to Mr Pickwick.

The first rule of English conversation is not making an ass of yourself. I had never met an MP before, even an un-elected one. I was taxed by nothing more intellectual than our genteel Churchford scandal until the *filet de boeuf* in the beam-ceilinged dining room. He solicited my opinion on The Bomb, 'as a doctor'.

'Unfortunately –' I sipped my Chambolle-Musigny. 'Outside their profession, doctors are no more perceptive, judicious or even rational than dockers.'

Jim smiled. 'So your job's to be an expert in one thing, an MP's to pretend he's an expert in everything?'

'Well, a comparative expert. The best doctors are the ones who best know what they don't know.'

I felt I was doing rather well.

He added, 'But surely the BMA says the National Health Service couldn't cope with the effects of a nuclear war?'

'Which is as obvious as saying that the Pompeii street cleaners couldn't cope with the effects of Vesuvius.'

'Then I shan't bother sending for an ambulance when the bomb drops on Churchford?'

'It won't,' I asserted. 'The world's peace is kept by a dog.'

They looked startled.

'Pavlov's dog,' I reassured them. 'Our rulers luckily all suffer from a conditioned fear reflex. Whoever started a war without a sporting chance of winning it? In the old days of armies and artillery it was easy, you just made sure that both of yours were bigger than the other lot's. Now you get a bomb back faster than a return of serve at Wimbledon.'

'You're an optimist,' murmured Charlotte.

'Optimism is the essential ingredient of all prescriptions,' I enlightened her.

'And if Richard's wrong,' Sandra pointed out, 'it's as painless as being wrong about an afterlife. When the occasion arises, it's too late to worry.'

'Well, someone agreed with your husband thirty years ago,' Jim informed her amiably. ' "We shall by a process of sublime irony have reached a stage where safety will be the sturdy child of terror, and survival the twin brother of annihilation." It never hurts a Parliamentary candidate to quote Winston Churchill.'

I felt flattered.

'So the Greenham ladies are wasting their time?' suggested Charlotte.

Jim sighed. 'CND! A useful political weapon. Not that it was ever much to do with nuclear ones. All these fashionable protest groups are interchangable, you know. Even self-appointed good causes provide spiritual intoxication for humdrum people, and let the nasty ones be as vicious as they want. We should like to become your private patients, Dr Gordon. Wouldn't we, darling?'

Charlotte nodded briskly.

So! I thought. The dinner party was an ambush. I had survived the critical crossfire. I felt even more flattered.

'You're just the nice, kind sort of old-fashioned doctor I'd like to look after me.' She smiled coyly at her husband. 'If ever I became pregnant.'

'We want Churchford to know we've a Churchford doctor, because we want Churchford to know we're firmly settled in Churchford.' Jim smiled again. 'After all, we've the overwhelming honour of finding ourselves neighbours of Sir Damian Havers.'

'One of my patients,' I disclosed modestly.

Sir Damian was the great actor, whose voice was compared in the Sunday papers to vast caverns in thunderstorms, the tumbling of distant avalanches, some mighty organ playing under water. I recalled that the bloody man had not paid his bill.

Sandra decided while driving home, 'Jim Whynn's a sinister young man.'

I was shocked. 'Why?'

'Anyone who can make himself so agreeable so easily is untrustworthy.'

I objected, 'But I impressed him.'

She sighed. 'Isn't there a danger, darling, that he might

5

just have thought you a man too small for his opinions?'

'Surely you're not saying I'm pompous?'

I was alarmed. There was a lot of it about at my time of life. But not in 'a good sort' like me?

'He wants to be a patient,' I reminded her. 'A politician of admirable judgement.'

'He's too tough for you to digest,' she warned gravely.

'All human beings are doctors' bread-and-butter,' I told her confidently.

I expected they were a couple of good sorts.

The election was shortly after the dinner party, in June. The constituency repaid the suckling.

Early the following October, Jim telephoned while I was enjoying the best drink of the day – morning tea in bed.

'I'm as fit as a flea,' he interrupted my congratulations. 'But I've something urgent and important to see you about. This evening?'

'That's enormously flattering,' I mentioned to Sandra.

'Be careful,' she cautioned again. 'Most politicians are hypocrites.'

'Hypocrisy's a civilized vice,' I countered. 'What causes more fuss in Britain than somebody telling us the truth?'

Jim opened the front door of the oast house himself. The circular sitting room was empty.

'Oh, the election was nothing, just securing my base,' he began warmly. 'Now the real battle starts! I think my toughest test so far was the Churchford party selection committee, raking through my family as though I was soliciting their daughters instead of their votes. And my father's been contributing handsomely to party funds for years,' he added resentfully.

He handed me a Scotch beside the log fire.

'I've taken Clem Attlee's advice to new MPs – specialize and keep out of the bars. And what more rewarding subject than the National Health Service?'

I murmured that helping to save life and spare suffering was always satisfying.

6

'All that, of course,' he said briefly, still standing. 'But don't you see the political beauty of the National Health Service? It touches everyone in the country before they're born and even after they're dead. Sickness has been turned from a family misery to a government policy. Like unemployment,' he reflected. 'Perhaps two mistakes? After all, millions of unemployed were on the cards once they'd invented the mechanical digger. Now, the National Health Service, like the quality of mercy, is twice bless'd. It heals the sick and provides a livelihood for many people who otherwise couldn't find one.'

'The biggest employer in Europe,' I mentioned.

He nodded vigorously. 'And a disgracefully inefficient one. But the gentlest snipping of incompetence naturally provokes outraged cries of "The Cuts!"'

He was speaking to me as Queen Victoria complained of Mr Gladstone, as if I was a public meeting.

'A firm must be efficient to afford pensions and medical care for its employees,' he continued fervently. 'Likewise a nation to afford a welfare state.'

His eyes glazed.

'We're a wonderful country, yet an utterly impossible one. We've invented everything from atom-splitting to bucks fizz, but the idea of putting ourselves out to please a customer is alien to our unconquerable spirit. Particularly if they're foreigners who don't even trouble to learn English.'

He pitched into his peroration.

'We're a magnificent nation of pirates! What is our glorious history? We've plundered all the rich countries of the world and made an empire of the poor ones. To echo Saki, Mr Sp – doctor, the British Empire was a good empire as empires go, and as empires go it went. Luckily, we still enjoy England's green and pleasant politics because we're living off the oil, as for two centuries we lived off the coal, with a couple of painful breaks for wars.'

'Bravo,' I said.

He flopped on the chintz sofa as on the green leather

House of Commons benches after a successful maiden speech.

I ventured, 'What about idealism?'

He laughed. 'To echo Johnson – idealism is the last refuge of a political scoundrel. Can you do something for me?'

From the Queen Anne bureau he produced a sheet of typewritten paper.

'You know this Royal Commission of the great and the good is reviewing the NHS from the consultants to the cleaners? Would you check some questions I'd like to ask about GPs? Naturally, I'm loading up with books, White Papers, reports,' he told me enthusiastically. 'An MP must master his brief like a QC, whether either knows his policy's a disaster or his client's a blackguard. That's why we so often appear to be talking drivel.'

I objected, 'But I've never been in the slightest interested in politics.'

'Dangerous, doctor! It's what an unfortunate French aristocrat complained on the steps of the guillotine. Do you know what the executioner said? *That* is precisely why you are here, and strapped him down.' He laughed again.

I promised to do my best. Jim saw me to the door.

'I hear you prefer single malt whisky?' he enquired. 'By the way, Charlotte's pregnant.'

Over the next two months I regularly brought front-line dispatches on the NHS to the oast house HQ. Our friendship grew from the mutual respect of professionals. Jim was as much a piece of political machinery as the works of Big Ben. He wanted to become prime minister. It was an amibition as altruistic as my own vocation. He felt it would so benefit the country.

'The PM's job's like an airline pilot's,' he lectured me. 'Manipulating the dials and levers and avoiding a crash. It doesn't need outstanding intelligence. The difficult bit's getting there. I know Walter Bagehot wrote about the magnificent training of gaining a seat, the ear, the confidence, of Parliament then your colleagues, but Disraeli was nearer by comparing the journey to climbing the greasy pole. Incidentally, I hear this Royal Commission's establishing a committee to advise the Government on general practice. I can get you a seat on it. How do you feel?'

'Alarmed, flattered and inadequate.'

'Paid, of course,' he added solemnly.

3

When Jim had telephoned the surgery for a consultation that April Friday over a year later, I was admitted to the oast house by a Norland nannie in a brown dress and a chocolate bow. I had organized the delivery of a son the previous May in the Churchford General's private wing by our most fashionable obstetrician Bertie Taverill – whose gynaecologist son Peter was blissfully to wed my daughter Jilly during the summer.

Jim and Charlotte were on the chintz sofa. She greeted me shortly and left. Jim rose and stood by the hearth.

'I got into trouble in London last night,' he announced.

I pushed my round glasses up my nose.

He laughed briefly. 'Don't worry, Richard. I wasn't arrested. And it was heterosexual.'

I was confused. Did I congratulate him?

'I've had a terrible week.'

He stood looking at his toes.

'It's a bloody abnormal life, an MP's. Everything happens at night. You're trapped in the House of Commons. Voting, there's always divisions in the Chamber.'

He paused, staring into the corner, and murmured, ' "This smelly, tawny male paradise", Chipps Channon MP once called it. It's like being aboard some vast liner with twenty-four-hour bars sailing nowhere in particular. I think a lot of members secretly like it. There's glamour working while others sleep – like a hospital? The Human Resources Bill. You've seen it in the papers?'

I nodded.

'We're having a rough ride, getting it through the House. The bigots seem to have combined with the fanatics.' He shuddered. 'You saw I took over in January as the Minister of Resources' Parliamentary Private Secretary?'

I nodded again. The job of 'PPS' was a pearl of great price, if no pay, for an MP with the ambition of them all, but not the years of most. Jim's predecessor had been killed in a car crash, infuriating the Prime Minister by provoking an awkward by-election.

'I'm having regrets. So has the Minister. How can I provide cheerful loyalty to a man who exudes incompetence instead of inspiration?' he asked bitterly. 'Last night I felt utterly wretched. I hadn't made the success of the job I'd expected. I was standing one of the lobby correspondents dinner in the House. They're a convivial lot on Fleet Street. I suppose I got rather pissed. "Alcohol enables Parliament to do things at eleven at night that no sane person would do at eleven in the morning." Shaw. Remember?' He smiled ruefully.

'I left Westminster about eleven. It was one of those nights you can never find a taxi. I started walking up Whitehall. To be honest, I wasn't keen to get home. I'd been alone in that Marylebone flat most of a fortnight. Charlotte has a load of committees and functions here in Churchford – it's essential for my seat that she's a local somebody. And there's the baby, of course,' he added as an afterthought.

'Thriving, I trust?'

'Oh, fine. Somehow I strayed into Soho.'

He stopped. He looked surprised at himself.

'I saw this bar, this club. Just a doorway with a flashing sign. I can't remember what, El something. I went in.' He sounded incredulous. 'Partly from curiosity. Partly because I couldn't face the empty flat. And partly because I wanted to look at something less depressing than benches of MPs. You just paid, and were a member. Rather easier than Boodle's in St James's. I gave a false name. Donald Duck. The man didn't seem ruffled. Perhaps a lot of their members are called the same. A drink, Richard?'

He poured me a whisky.

'Inside was pink, stuffy and dreadfully noisy. The sort of

11

music you hear from those radios people carry like suitcases. I sat at a table with a dirty pink cloth and a vase. A daffodil, I remember. I ordered a Scotch. A girl sat down. I said, have a drink. She said she only drank champagne. A bottle cost the earth, but I didn't care. It made such a nice change from Parliament. The girl asked if I'd like to go home with her. I said yes.'

'Was she nice?'

'Not bad.'

I nodded towards the door. 'Charlotte knows?'

'Of course.'

'And?'

He shrugged. 'It was an accident to which lonely MPs are liable. Were I a jockey, I'd get broken bones.'

I suggested tactfully, 'You're worried the girl's given you something more than a good time?'

He wrinkled his nose. 'Not really.' He poured himself some sherry from a Dartington decanter. 'I'm worried about *myself*. Should I see a psychiatrist?'

'No more than you'd call the fire brigade for a burn in the carpet.'

He contradicted me. 'I feel I should. Through sober eyes it's perfectly horrifying.'

'A lot of respectable men on any commuter train wouldn't give it a second thought.'

'But it would damage my career,' he exclaimed. 'If it got in the papers.'

'Why should it?'

'She might remember me.'

'A busy check-out girl can't remember her customers.'

He added uneasily, 'I may have said something about being an MP. It's incredible, infuriating! How women make madmen of us all.'

I observed, 'The public library shelves would be half-empty otherwise.'

'The revelation that I'd instantly seen a pyschiatrist,' he reasoned, 'would make the incident look a mental aberration which I'd hastened to repair, for the benefit of the voters I serve.'

There was silence.

'This Lagavulin is the pick of the Islay malts,' I remarked, raising my glass appreciatively.

He glanced at me quickly. 'Last week I thought of killing myself.'

'Oh?'

A suicide threat was a bird of ill-omen compared to a lark with a tart.

'By the way, that's something Charlotte doesn't know.'

I do not consign people readily to psychiatrists, who may lead them on a long journey to nowhere. My colleagues often find them useful for ridding themselves of awkward patients. In the spacious days when my father practised, he advised instead a long cruise.

'Taking an overdose now seems utterly ridiculous,' he continued forcefully. 'But it's frightening that I ever had the idea. And I *must* be fit, physically and mentally, now I've started to shin up that greasy pole.'

Jim was a tense, self-obsessed worrier whose career had a demanding egotism of its own. Perhaps a psychiatrist would do him good? Perhaps another girl in a Soho club would do better.

'If it makes you happy, I'll arrange for a chat with Dr Elmsworthy,' I agreed half-heartedly.

Jim seemed pleased. Though I felt mainly through winning the argument. 'Where's he keep his couch?'

'Psychiatry is horizontal only in comic cartoons. He shares consulting rooms in the private wing of the General – which you must have noticed when Charlotte had the baby, is tumbledown, congested and deeply suspect by the health-workers' unions.'

A political glint entered his lacklustre eye, as a sailor on a life raft recalled to the facts of navigation.

'Churchford needs a brand-new private sector hospital. I'll do something about it, once this odious business is past.

An admirable crusade for your local MP, don't you think?'

I usually referred patients to Dr Oliver Scuttle, who resembled the popular image of a psychiatrist as little as Nelson a sea dog. Ollie was on a sabbatical in Canada, leaving Walter Elmsworthy, a sharp-nosed, sharp-tongued, a wiry, pale little dark-haired man with the attitude of controlled despair towards his patients of a traffic policeman towards motorists.

A week later came a letter to my surgery.

Churchford General Hospital
Private Wing

Dear Richard,

Thank you for sending me Mr Whynn.

He is suffering from feelings of inefficiency and inadequacy, causing depression with possibly suicidal tendencies. There is anxiety that he will respond similarly in the more responsible governmental posts which he confidently expects later to be offered.

He is also anxious about recently spending a night (or lesser period) with a prostitute when drunk. I feel he suffers less from guilt than fears that the episode might impede his achievement of high political office, towards which he displays a ruthless determination.

His marriage is stable. He is financially far better provided for than he cares to admit for political reasons.

The symptoms are of recent origin, and there is no history of depressive illness or anxiety neurosis.

I consider this a temporary disorder, occasioned by a personal dislike developed for his superior, the Minister of Resources, whom he describes somewhat scathingly as 'unfit to run the spare-parts department in a garage'.

I wish to see him again in three months for reassessment. Meanwhile, he should take a rest from his official duties. I do not feel that antidepressants are indicated.

I assured My Whynn that the episode would in time seem but a bizarre deviation in the successful career he has planned for himself.

I hope to see you and Sandra at the Friends of the General sherry party.

Yours sincerely,

Walter

Dr Walter Elmsworthy
MD, MRCP, MRCPsych.

These confidences were spread over the front page of my Sunday paper.

4

The telephone was already ringing.

'Richard Gordon? You swine. You louse. You shit.'

It was Charlotte, cross.

'What did you get for it? Thirty pieces of silver, I suppose? Have you no decency? No shame? No loyalty? Honour? Honesty? Humanity?'

'I er –'

'Where have you been all night? In hiding? A wonder you haven't fled the country.'

It was the golf club annual ball.

'Do you realize what a terrible time I'm having? Those friends on Fleet Street, ringing me every five minutes. Reporters overrunning the garden like rats. A vast TV van in the lane, looks settled for months. My God! I can hear a helicopter overhead.'

'Look, Charlotte –'

'And a call . . . a call at midnight . . . from Chequers.' Her voice broke. 'Ruined. My Jim's career. He'll never be a minister now, not even some utterly ludicrous one like agriculture or the arts.'

'I can explain –'

'Thank God he's inaccessible in Zambia. I've been trying Lusaka all night, but it's engaged. Oh Christ! What shall I do?'

'Might I suggest –'

'I'm going to have you struck off. I'm going to haul you through the courts. I'm going to bankrupt you with damages. I'm going to see you in jail. I'm going to have your entire family shunned by every decent person in Churchford.'

'I can understand –'

'My God, if I wasn't a woman I'd come and beat the living daylights out of you. If I ever have to set eyes on you again, I wouldn't trust myself from flying at your throat with a meat knife, and to hell with the consequences.'

'I er –'

'Goodbye.'

This was difficult to handle in pyjamas, and still wanting an early morning pee.

Sandra in bed upstairs in her M & S broderie anglaise nightie caught my alarming expression over the steaming Teasmade.

'Darling! Something awful with a patient?'

I silently laid the paper on our flowered coverlet. It was more infuriatingly not our trigger-happy vulgar Sunday paper, but the genteel one with the book reviews, discriminating articles about wine and undiscriminating ones about women, and lots on Provençale cookery.

She saw the headline, MINISTER'S AIDE WITH VICE GIRL – 'INEFFICIENT, SUICIDAL'.

She gasped.

'Surely you didn't reveal all this to some reporter?' she broke off reading.

'Of course I didn't,' I told her testily.

'I mean, late at night in the bar of the golf club?'

'Doctors don't break the Hippocratic Oath even when they've had a few. Otherwise, it would be a pretty meaningless oath, wouldn't it?'

'Thank God it doesn't mention you or Walter Elmsworthy by name.'

'Only so we can't sue them, I suppose', I said morosely. 'Every word in that "Report from an eminent psychiatrist" was in the letter he sent me last Friday.'

'Where is it now?' she asked worriedly.

'Locked in the surgery files. I hope.'

'Someone broke in and stole it,' she exclaimed. 'They're always trying with the drugs.'

I decided miserably, 'I'd better go and see, hadn't I? That

17

was Charlotte on the phone. Now I know how Guy Fawkes felt, trying to explain away all those barrels of gunpowder.'

'Perhaps *she* told the press?' Sandra suggested brightly. 'Revenge for that harlot in Soho. You never know how a woman's mind works.'

'Any woman who ruins even her outside chance of becoming the Prime Minister's wife is not vengeful, but insane.'

Sandra added instinctively, 'Do you suppose it will reflect on our children?'

'Striking them off as well would be rather Old Testament vengeance, even for the General Medical Council.'

She kissed me dramatically. 'Darling! I shall stand by you.'

'Thank you.'

A wife becomes of awesome importance in a crisis, like the everyday unheeded fire escape.

I hastily shaved. I pulled on my golf clothes. I was booked for a round at ten with Jack Windrush, pathologist at the General (with the medical student sense of humour). Sandra fussed about missing my breakfast.

'Perhaps it will all blow over,' she suggested cheeringly as I left. 'Wasn't it Mr Gladstone who said a week was a long time in politics?'

I drove the mile to Chaucer Way feeling like Jim Whynn's cautionary French aristocrat bumping along in the tumbril.

The busy newsagents were celebrating the first rite of an English Sunday, buying the papers. The succeeding rituals of a pint in the pub and the roast beef would be spiced with Jim Whynn's shame. It must have already sweetened the cornflakes of his rival Parliamentary candidate Bert Bullivant. He had done unexpectedly well in the election, the darling of the New Town with its bawling infant University.

I unlocked the front door. The surgery on Sunday had the forlorn hollowness of a school during the holidays. I tremulously entered the small back room with the grey metal files. I sweatingly unlocked the private patients' cabinet. I said phew.

18

The telephone was already ringing.

'Richard? Walter. Sandra said you were there. What the hell's going on?'

I perched on the desk of my small, custard-coloured consulting room.

'Your letter's safe,' I reassured him cheerfully. 'I'm holding it.'

'Who did you show it to?' he demanded.

'Bloody nobody!' I exclaimed. 'Not even my partners.'

'Then your receptionist must have seen it,' he suggested brusquely.

I was stung. 'Rather than disclose confidential information about patients to the papers, my Mrs Jenkins would perform sex acts live on dais at the next BMA meeting.'

'Oh, you can't trust anyone these days,' he told me, like Caesar's ghost addressing Brutus.

I countered forcefully, 'What about your Mrs Proudfoot?'

'I've just phoned her. She's going to the General to check the carbon of my letter's safe in the psychiatric department files.'

'I'd better drive to your place.'

'Yes, I think you had,' he agreed irritably.

I put down the telephone. I was angry at Walter's suspicion that I had mishandled the letter. This was mixed with uneasiness at my own suspicion that perhaps I had.

Walter Elmsworthy had a gabled house with a pretty garden a mile past the General on the London road. He was in the sun-flooded sitting room wearing jeans and a scarlet sports shirt. Opposite stood Lynda Proudfoot clothed in misery.

'It's gone,' said Walter doomfully.

I adroitly turned a sigh of relief into a sneeze.

'*I* haven't leaked, doctor, honestly, I just can't understand it,' she insisted, near tears. She was pretty, brown-haired, married to an assistant administrator at the hospital. 'I've always done exactly the same, all the years I've been working for you, once we've finished in the private wing I take all the letters I've typed back to the department and lock the copies in the files, I'm sure that's what I did last Thursday, look, here's the key, safe in my purse with my donor card.'

I suggested to Walter, 'Someone picked the lock?'

'Who?'

'One of Jim Whynn's political enemies.'

'Oh, a Churchford Watergate,' he said sarcastically.

'Perhaps it was blackmail? The victim bravely refused to pay up.'

'In my experience, he cravenly always does.'

'I submit my resignation,' Lynda said quickly.

'Wouldn't hear of it,' muttered Walter.

'I must. It's my responsibility.'

'Oh, no, no, no.'

'I insist.'

'Very well, then.'

She gasped. She stared. She jammed her knuckles in her mouth. She fled from the room, the house, into her car, slamming all three doors.

It was dreadfully harrowing. I was desperate for a large Scotch, and had not yet had breakfast.

Walter crossed to the telephone, scowling. 'I'll get the police.'

'What's the point? The harm's done. Why stir up more fuss?' I nodded after her. 'Haven't we upset Lynda enough for one day?'

He gave the newspaper a look of loathing. 'Then I'll phone the editor.'

'There'll be nobody there,' I pointed out. 'He'd only laugh in our faces. They guard their informants like we our professional secrets. It's the freedom of the press. Though personally I see nothing wrong with the old custom of sticking journalists now and then in the pillory.'

'We must do *something*,' he declared impatiently.

'Why? Masterly inactivity is often the wisest course in surgery and in life.'

Walter shrugged. 'It must have been an inside job. Who else would know of Lynda's routine? One of the cleaners,' he decided. 'The Health Service takes on people I don't care sharing the same roof with. 'It's a scandal the NHS can't provide my department with up-to-date typing and copying equipment. I'm desperate for a computer, I might have been asking for half-a-dozen body scanners. The cuts!' he muttered disgustedly.

I exclaimed, '*The Case of the Purloined Letter*! Have you read it? Never did I imagine I should be embroiled in Edgar Allan Poe for real.'

He shook his head testily. He did not seemingly appreciate literary comparisons.

I looked at my watch. I was amazed. Barely 8.30. Sandra was right, no point in missing breakfast. Particularly as Sunday was cholesterol day. I left him staring irritably through the window. I wanted to sit alone and collect my thoughts. I decided to cancel the golf. Even Nero did not start his own fire.

My daughter was already at home. Peter Teverill was coming for lunch.

Jilly is blonde and slender, and like many lady practitioners inclined to be bossy. I found her amazingly unconcerned about the morning's public outrage. I supposed that when you are young and shortly to be married even impending nuclear incineration, unsuccoured by the NHS, lies far from the forefront of your mind.

'Phone a lawyer at the Medical Defence Union,' she urged. 'They get you out of ethical scrapes of all sorts.'

'What a bloody silly suggestion on a Sunday morning,' I pointed out.

'Oh, they've a hot line for doctors taken in adultery, or whatever,' she murmured, in an armchair reading the vile newspaper.

'That letter was extracted from the files by someone who knew exactly what they were looking for and exactly how to make the foulest use of it,' I told her, while I was

21

volupturizing in bacon-and-eggs. I wondered, 'Does much get stolen in the General?'

'Really, daddy, surely you know larceny's the commonest complaint seen in the Health Service?' she enquired pityingly. 'Everything from the surgeon's credit cards to the patient's toffees while both are in the theatre. I sometimes wonder if I need bother to remove stitches.'

'If I keep my head down,' I calculated sagely, 'nobody in Churchford need know that Jim Whynn is one of my patients.'

'Everybody in Churchford knows that Jim Whynn is one of your patients.'

'Why?'

'You told them all yourself.'

It was a glorious weekend of bursting buds and birdsong. I noticed neither. I felt like a murderer whose strictly private business with the victim has astoundingly and alarmingly become public property.

I tried all Sunday morning telephoning Charlotte, but she had unhooked the instrument of torture. My partner, motherly Dr Elaine Spondek, telephoned consolingly.

So did Dr Quaggy.

'Richard, I'm so sorry about this appalling mess you're in.'

His voice dripped like emulsified vitriol.

'You were quite justified, you know, Richard, feeling so proud that our local MP had selected you in preference to all the rest of us GPs in Churchford. I *do* hope you won't let this isolated incident – however disastrous – spoil your happy retirement from such a long and distinguished career among us.'

'I am not bloody retiring,' I shouted. 'I am medicine's Frank Sinatra.'

'You're *not?*' He expressed pained surprise. 'I'm awfully sorry, but I was only repeating the impression which all your patients seem to be getting.'

I rattled down the telephone.

22

'That vulture in dove's clothing!'

'Oh, everyone knows he wants to get rid of you, to oil his son Arnold into the gap,' remarked Jilly, now reading *Recent Advances in Surgery*.

'But if you're *not* retiring, darling, does it matter?' asked Sandra.

'Quaggy's been telling the entire population of Churchford in strict confidence for months that I've decided to go,' I complained bitterly. 'And rumours fulfil themselves, as winds blow ships on the rocks.'

'Arnold Quaggy was known by us fellow-students at St Swithin's as a tapeworm with bulimia,' said Jilly. 'The new overeating disease,' she explained condescendingly.

'Perhaps I *should* retire,' I suggested sombrely. 'We could live in the Algarve and enjoy weather like this all year round. I know how you yearn for sunshine all winter, my dear,' I told Sandra affectionately. 'Like a root vegetable.'

'If you retired, daddy, you'd be like Jesus without any sinners,' decided Jilly.

I found that I had unthinkingly picked up the pestiferous paper.

'Why has medicine become so complicated since it was a simple matter of making people better?' I complained crossly, throwing it over the room.

Peter Taverill arrived at midday. Lunch was gloomy.

'Have you any idea about a wedding day?' asked Sandra with reined impatience during the roast duck.

'It's awfully difficult, mum, with me working here in Churchford and Peter doing this gynae registrar's job in the Midlands,' Jilly complained.

'Those whom God hath joined together the NHS puts asunder,' Peter pronounced.

'Because of medical unemployment, and this terrible scramble for jobs, and having to go wherever you can get one,' Jilly continued unhappily, 'marriages between young doctors have a terrifying divorce rate.'

'More victims of the cuts,' sighed Peter cheerfully.

23

Peter Taverill was good-looking and well-dressed. At medical school he had won all the scholarships and prizes he fancied. Having the ready charm found in gynaecologists and disc jockeys, he perseveringly implied that I knew more than he did.

'Of course, the pill has a failure rate of 0.16 per cent, intra-uterine devices 1.5 per cent, spermicidal jelly 11.9 per cent, and female sterilization 0.13 per cent,' he recited over the rhubarb tart, adding quickly, 'As you know full well, Richard.'

This made me feel so wretchedly ignorant I nervously retaliated by expounding on the general practitioner as the true heir of Hippocrates, the doctor who studied the entire patient and his environment. I became terrified that I was being pompous.

Television news that evening announced that Jim was flying home from Lusaka. It also presented the villainous paper's editor – slight, bushy-haired, inoffensive and shameless.

With the glowing satisfaction of a man discovering his duty felicitously coinciding with his desires, he insisted that a psychiatrist's report on an MP liable to such squalid conduct was of national importance and demanded publication. He confessed no notion how the letter had strayed into his Fleet Street office.

'The doorman found it on the lobby floor.' He grinned. 'Perhaps it blew off the back of a passing lorry?'

'What do you suppose the Government's reaction will be?' Sandra asked as we went to bed.

I considered. 'One of profound regret, 'I told her. 'That the rack is no longer freely available in EC3.'

5

On Monday morning I went as usual to the surgery. Two detectives had got there first.

Mrs Jenkins my receptionist was aghast. Mrs Flowerbutts our floor-lady was aquiver. I greeted them ashen-faced. A police car in my driving-mirror always makes me feel like Jack the Ripper.

They were a young sergeant and a constable with the keen, cheerful, pink-faced air of a golf pro and his assistant. They presented a typed list of a dozen burglaries since the surgery was opened. I had forgotten them like parking tickets.

They inspected the files. They politely asked after suspects. They invited themselves back.

As they left, I telephoned the psychiatric department at the General.

'I've got four of them,' Walter said gloomily. 'Photographing and taking fingerprints and asking stupid questions. My morning's work is impossible. It's quite outrageous, affecting patients like this. I only wish I knew what was happening.'

'Whatever it is, you and I are in the national bedpan,' I informed him.

I need never buy newspapers. The headlines which every morning rustle round our mustard-coloured waiting room provide a broad review of the press. Its evil eye that Monday had swivelled to the Minister of Resources from Jim, whose corrosive assessment of his boss they gleefully endorsed.

The Minister was already installed in Fleet Street's Chamber of Horrors, through a tetchy disdain towards those who did not share his opinions, particularly of himself. I agreed warmly with the papers. The man was the insufferable Minister of Health whose career suffered from a violent attack of bellyache on television, while sycophantically sampling the new Government-sponsored cheese, as my patients may remember.

When I told Sandra about the detectives at lunchtime she responded that absolutely everybody in Churchford knew for certain it was me who had leaked the psychiatric report. I groaned with the frustration of Captain Dreyfus on Devil's Island.

Television that evening had Jim arriving at Heathrow. He stood with hands deep in the pockets of his belted raincoat, tersely offering his regret at the embarrassment caused the Prime Minster, the Government and his family, in that order. I sat at Sandra's escritoire and laboriously wrote a note to Charlotte, so wretchedly painful it might have been for the enlightenment of my relatives after hanging myself.

The grandfather clock in the hall was chiming midnight as I set foot on the stairs for bed. The telephone rang.

I grabbed it.

'Jim?'

Silence.

I said hello several times. Heavy breathing. An obscene phone call? A threatening one? Some people enjoyed being anonymously vile to others in adversity.

'Is that the doctor?' came unmistakably.

It was Sir Damian Havers, with a voice like some groaning ageless oak in a tempest.

'What's the matter?' I asked tetchily.

'I am dying.'

I allowed for dramatic effect. Sir Damian was dying if he caught a cold or his finger in his Rolls door.

'What are you dying *of*?' I demanded.

'I have the ague, I rather fancy.'

'Won't tomorrow morning do?' I suggested impatiently.

'Tomorrow *morning*? I fear I shall not linger on this earth long enough for that.'

I hesitated.

It is a harsh rule of medicine that even hypochondriacs become ill. I had misfortune enough with my practice already. Then I recalled that the damned fellow owed me the best part of a thousand quid. Whenever I had mentioned it, Sir Damian made the graceful gesture of Antonio dismissing Shylock and murmured, 'My agent will attend to it, dear boy, I have absolutely no head for money, I just wouldn't know how to buy a three-ha'penny stamp in a post office.'

'I'll be there shortly,' I agreed grumpily.

I returned to the escritoire, scribbled a bill for professional services rendered, pocketed it, and shouted to Sandra that I had been called out. Cold meals and cold beds are commonplaces in any medical marriage.

I drove through moonlit lanes towards Buskins, Sir Damian's seat overlooking the Weald of Kent. Our successful actors are as avid as our successful politicians to become country gentlemen. I reflected that Sir Damian's addiction to mortality was aggravated by his specializing in Shakespeare. The Bard's actors like his cowards are required to die many times before their deaths. Hamlet, Othello, Macbeth and all the plum parts have the curt stage direction *Dies* as the audience is restively starting to think of a nice steak-and-chips with a half-bottle of Beauj.

A handful of actors – like Nigel Vaughan the TV star I had saved from being written out of the script of life – lived within pleasant reach of the West End in Churchford. They made enthusiastic patients. Mummers come running in tears brandishing the sore place for Nanny, because they enjoy the Peter Pan syndrome. They convert childhood dressing-up and let's-pretend into hard cash, in Sir Damian's case vast quantities of.

I reached his black-timbered, sagging-roofed Elizabethan mansion. Every leaded window was ablaze, like a stage set. Was I to be engulfed in some sparkling showbiz party? I listened. The house was as chillingly silent as an empty theatre. I reached for the wrought-iron pull beside the

27

studded skewed front door. The bell clanged as dramatically as the Inchcape Rock.

Light footsteps approached. The door creaked open. It was Herbert, Sir Damian's friend. He was skinny, parchment-faced, gingery (dyed), wore skin-tight jeans and walked as if balancing along a tightrope.

I asked, 'What's wrong?'

Herbert giggled. 'AIDS, I shouldn't be a bit surprised.'

I entered the stone-flagged hall. There seemed only the pair of them in the stark, draughty, echoing house. Herbert made a moue.

'Lobster thermidor after the show,' he suggested severely. 'I ask you! It's her own fault. Over-indulgence, I told her straight. Sometimes I think she makes herself an absolute martyr to her stomach. She ought to know better at her age, even the one she tells the newspapers.'

I followed Herbert up the oak staircase. Sir Damian was of course a queer Lear.

'Here's the doctor, dear,' Herbert announced, more reproving than reassuring.

He opened the door of a beamed, bare-boarded room with a massive tapestry-hung four-poster, worthy to be the death-bed of Shakespearian kings, except for the frilly pink pillows and teddy bear.

Sir Damian had a jaw like a shovel and eyebrows recalling a pair of sleeping Skye terriers. Thick grey hair cascaded towards his bony shoulders, his eyes glowed as fiercely as a pair of theatrical spotlights, his cheeks looked as hollow as Yorick's.

He declared in a voice like the soughing of wind through historic battlements, 'I rather fancy I am feeling a little better. Herbert, be a darling and fetch up a bottle of bubbly.'

'Really! I've never heard of such a thing.'

Herbert slapped Damian's wrist.

'Oh, don't be so rotten,' said Sir Damian.

Herbert elegantly flicked a hand.

'It's for your own good, dear. I wouldn't have *your* insides, not for all the tights in Berman's.'

'But don't you remember Hull?' Sir Damian demanded majestically. 'I was saved by Cliquot when I was dying, that night I got caught short in the breach at Harfleur.'

Herbert rested knuckles on hip.

'No, sweetie,' he contradicted. 'Hull was that dreadful woman who started to give birth in the stalls. Quite ruined your blow, winds, and crack your cheeks bit.'

Sir Damian's chiselled look mellowed to a king recalling battles long ago. 'Was it at Stoke-on-Trent, the cockroach in my wig during the balcony scene?'

'*No, darling*, that was Portsmouth. Stoke was the mouse up Titania's furbelows.'

Both laughed. 'Surely I remember something in Cardiff, Herbert?'

'Yes, dear, the theatre caught fire.'

'So it did,' Sir Damian pronounced solemnly. 'They all demanded their money back. The management was quite right, reimbursing only the ones who had been somewhat burnt.'

I coughed.

'Ah, the doctor,' he recalled cheerfully. 'You must read about it in my autobiography *All the World's a Stage Worse*. Just published, utterly fantastic reviews, but of course you'll have studied them.'

He sighed like the breeze rustling immemorial elms.

'Perhaps my real role in life was to be some great author like . . . like . . . who *was* there, Herbert? Dickens!'

He reached towards the bedside-table with the pink-shaded lamp.

'As it happens, I have a few copies here. And you shall have one, doctor. *And* I shall sign it.'

I stammered thanks for the gracious favour.

'You'll be utterly enthralled by the stories about our two darling Sir Johns,' he promised, flourishing ballpoint across flyleaf. 'And fascinated by my ingenious theories on our demanding art.'

He presented me with the book. I had noticed from the handful among my patients, that actors have a charming delusion their work is more significant than a Punch and Judy show on the sands of time.

'I'd better examine you, Sir Damian.'

'Oh, I feel perfectly well now, thank you. But it was kind of you to come.'

'For my own good, not yours,' I pointed out firmly, pulling down the bedclothes. 'You don't want the bother of suing me for overlooking a perforated ulcer, do you?'

'I just happen to think these see-through nighties more comfortable for sleeping in,' he mentioned.

I found nothing wrong. It was flame-coloured. I tried unsuccessfullly to identify his perfume.

I said, 'Have a couple of these white tablets if there's any more indigestion. And might I take this opportunity of presenting my account? It doesn't include the present visit.'

He took the paper. He read it with eyebrows quivering and drawn together, resembling a pair of Skye terriers copulating.

'Famine is in thy cheeks, need and oppression starveth in thy eyes, contempt and beggary hangs upon thy back,' he observed in a voice like an echo from a tomb.

'Things in the NHS aren't quite as bad as that,' I countered.

'I was Romeo talking to his apothecary. And that fellow only wanted forty ducats. Herbert, see to this some time.' Sir Damian passed him the bill disposively. 'And I rather fancy a Welsh rarebit.'

'I am *not* going messing about with sticky hot cheese at this hour,' Herbert objected petulantly.

'Yes, you are,' Sir Damian assured him. 'Or you'll be back to performing in the Leicester Square gents.'

Outside the bedroom, Herbert rubbed thumb and forefinger in my face. 'The cash.'

'Ah! You've got it handy?'

'For the autobiography. The price is on the jacket. This

isn't a public library you know. Why, there's thirty-six pictures of her in it for your money.'

I reached for my wallet. I felt it all took my mind off Jim Whynn.

6

Next morning's papers announced that Jim Whynn had resigned his government job.

It was the worst week of my life, and only Tuesday.

At surgery I had another of Walter Elmsworthy's private patients.

Douglas Blackadder was a City accountant, a Churchford councillor, and an old friend. He had asked me to care for his nineteen-year-old daughter Annabel, as wayward as many of the young before their psychological mechanism has run itself in – pot, CND, shoplifting, the conventional protests against convention.

She was pretty, pale, with long untended fair hair, in calf-length jeans and pink pumps, a proclamatory T-shirt, no bra, no make-up, several rings on her fingers and piercing her ears.

Walter's report was short. He was an unlikeable man but a sensible psychiatrist. He prescribed only 'TLC' – tender loving care, the healer long before doctors became mankind's busybodies.

I told her comfortingly across the consulting desk, 'These troubles of yours are only mental growing pains, Annabel. You mustn't feel you're a misfit, who's going to end up in a home, or somewhere more alarming. In a year or so you'll be astounded, wondering how you managed to rub the world up the wrong way.' I smiled. 'At least you didn't get in the papers.'

She gulped.

'Dr Gordon –'

She paused.

I enquired mildly, 'You haven't got yourself into more trouble since you saw Dr Elmsworthy?'

'Oh, no,' she said sharply. 'Not really. Well. Perhaps. Sort of.'

She continued quickly, 'In that private patients' place at the General Hospital, you wait to see the doctor sitting with the typewriter lady, well, she left the room for something and I just happened to read the letters on her desk, one was about Mr Whynn so I slipped the copy into my jeans pocket, I mean, it's a public scandal, isn't it?' she insisted shrilly. 'If I hadn't seen it, everything would have been hushed up for ever, wouldn't it? I mean, well, my conscience is clear, absolutely, clear as soap bubbles in the sunlight.'

She laughed.

My hair porcupined.

'That was very naughty,' I observed, when I removed my hands from my face.

'Well, if the letter was that important they shouldn't have left it hanging about,' she vindicated herself tartly. 'They didn't even notice it was gone. The lady showed me out all smiles.'

I sighed. 'Do you realize, my dear Annabel, what a lot of misery you caused?'

'It wasn't me who brought the misery. He did it himself. Didn't he? I mean, that sex,' she reasoned pertly.

She suddenly looked into the far corner of the consulting room and said miserably, 'When I found the letter I wasn't going to put it in the newspapers. I didn't know what I was going to do with it. I was really frightened. Once I was outside the hospital I thought of taking it back, but I couldn't, they'd be so angry with me. I thought instead I'd tear it up. I wish I had, I wish I had.'

She sat staring, blinking.

'Then how *did* it get into the newspapers?' I persisted.

'It was this other MP. That same night I was going to a disco in London, in Camden Town, it was Youth For . . . I don't know what. I met him there, oh, he was really charming.' Her expression lightened. 'Just like any ordinary person, dancing with everybody.'

33

'He was an MP on the other side to Mr Whynn?'
She nodded.
'That's right. You know my politics aren't Mr Whynn's. Nor my dad's, come to that. So I said, Did he know Mr Whynn? And he laughed and said, "Who doesn't, Mr Whynn sees to that." And I said, laughing too, that I knew something about Mr Whynn which no one else did. And he was suddenly very interested and asked what it was. I don't know, I'd never even talked to an MP before, but I supposed I ought to tell him all the things he wanted to know, anyway, he went on about it, so I took the letter out of my pocket and let him read it.'
She stopped.
'I imagined he'd just make a joke and give it back, but he looked awfully serious and said, "A man like that doesn't deserve to represent ordinary decent people in Parliament. It goes to prove what we all think, the only interests he's got at heart are his own. And this sordid sex." He said it was my duty as a citizen to expose it. Suddenly I was quite terrified. I was getting mixed up in something I didn't really understand. But he put his arm round me and squeezed me tight and said, "Don't worry, Annabel, I personally give you my word of honour as a Member of Parliament to protect you from any consequences." Those were his actual words. And as I said, he was gorge, so I just nodded, and he said, "Don't go away while I make a phone call." In five minutes he was back, and said, "Go to this newspaper office, take a taxi, here's the fare." By then I just seemed to get carried along, there was a woman downstairs waiting for me, she took me up to a room with only the editor himself, you saw him on the telly.'
I nodded.
'He said, "It's in the national interest to expose this nasty story, you were a brave girl to risk getting hold of it." Then I was frightened again, because I never thought I'd done anything daring, or even very wrong, I mean, it was only a letter, wasn't it? I said to him, "I hope I won't get into any

trouble," and he said, "No way, like any editor I always protect my . . . my . . . " '

'Sources of information?' I supplied.

'That's right. And he squeezed me, too.'

'Did he give you any money?'

She looked amazed. 'Oh, no.'

'How did you react next morning, with it all over the headlines?'

She shrugged. 'Funny, but it didn't seem anything to do with me. Perhaps I was a bit shocked. Daddy thought I was sickening for something.'

We stared at each other. I felt a horrifying if misplaced responsibility for the catastrophe. Belloc's Aunt, returning from that interesting play *The Second Mrs Tanqueray*, to find mendatious Matilda and the House were Burned, must inescapably have felt the same.

'I'm the only person in the world you can talk to about this?'

She nodded.

I decided, 'What's done cannot be undone. That's the most comforting way of contemplating any misdeeds. I advise you to keep quiet about it.'

She asked with childish uncertainty, 'But I did right, didn't I?'

'I don't know. I'm the doctor, not the vicar.'

She startled me by giggling. 'But it's all exciting, isn't it? I mean, I've done something quite terrific to the Government. Something hardly anyone else could do. Anyway, they deserve it, look at, well, police brutality against strikers, and that.'

She left.

I groaned.

I telephoned Walter Elmsworthy. His new secretary said he had cancelled his consultations and taken a few days leave. No one knew where. He needed peace. I was relieved. A man undergoing torture does not take kindly to recrimination.

The Hippocratic Oath was plain. *Whatever I see or hear, professionally or privately, which ought not to be divulged, I will keep secret and tell no one.* This is not to sanctify the doctor but to unmuzzle the patient. The truth may be more hurtful than the disease, but the doctor may need it to cure the case. Sufferers from the effects of bullets, or of swallowing contraband diamonds or drugs, must seek treatment without risking the surgery leading to the cells. Our ethics are as practical as the rest of medicine.

Annabel was a headstrong and exploited youngster. I could discuss her with Walter or another doctor. If I divulged her secrets to Jim, to her father, to the detectives, to anyone, Aesculapius the God of Healing could rightly have burst into the surgery and clobbered me with his snake-twined staff.

I was late home for lunch. Sandra stared at my expression in alarm. She asked, 'God! What's happened now?'

I murmured migraine.

The Oath! It chafed like a strait-jacket.

The marriage bed should never be bolstered with secrets – except of course those likely to get you smartly kicked out of it – but I was always reluctant to impart my darker professional gossip. I was somehow one flesh with my patients as well as my wife.

Sandra said, 'Migraine? You've never had migraine before.'

'Well, I've got it now.'

'You're far too old to start migraine. It always begins in the twenties.'

I demanded, 'Who's the doctor, then?'

She said, 'Really! If you want to match tenderness with boorishness, you can eat your lunch alone.'

She slammed the kitchen door. I wondered if Hippocrates was married.

Wednesday. The weather turned depressingly freezing.

I now opened the morning papers as I checked through letters about my patients from our local St Ethelnoth's

Hospice, one of life's termini. These were invariably as much bad news as a banshee's wail.

Fleet Street had found the tart. Mrs Maureen Flynn, twenty-five, pretty, dark, fringed, was sitting in a spotted dress at her fireside as modestly as any other Notting Hill housewife. Jim had been a real gentleman. With two children, she had to make ends meet since Mr Flynn went to the races one morning and never came back. The public encountered also Mr Vella, the club's proprietor, who denied indignantly the slightest knowledge of private arrangements between his members and their dancing partners. He should never let in MPs, he complained, they always caused trouble.

I felt sadder for poor Jim Whynn. He had exchanged the butt of scandal for one of ridicule. A public man's publicized sex-life deserved the style set by our kings and their courtesans. He must have felt like a Victorian paterfamilias confronted with the housemaid's baby.

I arrived for morning surgery shortly after the two detectives.

The sergeant asked if I had developed any suspicions.

'None whatever.'

'No clue has come to light, doctor?'

'Not the slightest.'

I moved uncomfortably in my consulting room chair. I fancied he was eyeing me like Sherlock Holmes telling the Hound of the Baskervilles, 'Sit!'

'Would you be prepared to make a statement to that effect, doctor?'

'Of course.'

I would sign it at Churchford police station the following afternoon.

I was committing a crime. Perjury? Perversion of justice? High treason? I had no option.

As they left, Mrs Jenkins said that Jim's secretary had telephoned asking me to call, and Sir Damian Havers would love to discuss my bill.

I drove to the oast house instead of home for lunch. A crowd of newspapermen hung round the gate. Several took my photograph. I felt horribly guilty this meant they knew my secret. They probably even snapped Jim's milkman.

Charlotte opened the front door. She said she was sorry for being so abusive. I kept my distance, I fancied she still had the meat knife in mind.

Jim was impressively self-controlled.

'Who did it?' he asked mildly, when we were alone in the circular sitting room.

'We shall never find out.'

'We shall,' he corrected me firmly. 'The big guns of Scotland Yard and MI5 have been targeted on it. You know how sensitive the Government is about leaks, God knows!'

I said humbly, 'I'm sorry you felt obliged to resign.'

'I didn't. I was sacked. Our politics retain their medieval savagery. Fortunately, they don't complete the job by cutting your head off as well.'

I added in the same tone, 'I'm sure all Churchford hopes you'll continue representing us in Parliament.'

'Oh, there's not the remotest possibility of resigning my seat,' he assured me. 'The Government couldn't possibly risk a by-election at the moment.'

'Your party leaders *did* seem pretty harsh on you. They must enjoy singularly high morals.'

'They haven't higher morals than the rest of us. The sweets of office are labelled "Humbug".'

He stared through the wide window at the lovely, tidy, expensive Kent countryside.

'It was my own fault,' he reflected. 'I remember what Dr Johnson once told Fanny Burney – "I am prevented many frolics that I should like very well since I am become such a theme for the papers". Perhaps I could have brazened out the girl. But your psychiatrist's letter did for me. My remarks about the Minister weren't exactly welcome. Though everyone knows his appointment was as intelligent as making a park-keeper Minister of the Environment.'

He fell silent.

'I'm not out in the cold alone,' he continued musingly. 'Every parliament sees a steady growth of dissatisfied or disillusioned MPs. Some have been sacked from government jobs, some are bitter they never had one, some can't stomach the prime minister – they are not generally likable persons – some find blunted the axes they came to the House to grind. It's easy to feel frustrated when the Government handles MPs like a pack of cards to be played in the Parliamentary game. With a comfortable majority, the work becomes as unexciting as the pay, and the Devil's never far from West-minster to find work for idle hands.'

His voice dropped to the conspiratorial. 'They mutiny whenever it's safe without doing a favour for the opposition – the issues don't much matter, a buccaneer with a sharp nose for political doubloons can fashion any handy implement into a weapon. Maybe I'll join the crew.'

He turned to face me.

'You and Dr Elmsworthy are responsible for the loss of that letter, however it was effected.'

I bowed my head.

'Obviously, we can't go on being your patients. I felt I should tell you that myself, because we've looked upon you as a family friend over the past couple of years.'

I bowed my head lower.

'We shall have to pick someone else in Churchford. I hear Dr Quaggy is highly thought of.'

I wished I could bow myself through the floor.

I slipped from the front door, through the reporters, into my car. I did not want any lunch. I did not want to be seen in Churchford. I had lost friends, patients, reputation, probably soon my liberty. I could retain all four by denouncing Anna-bel. Which was unthinkable. I decided to drive down the road and call on Sir Damian. Best to strike while the gold was hot.

He was in a brocade dressing-gown by a log fire in a vast hearth, taking a fork lunch of truffle omelette and cham-pagne.

'Herbert and I were organizing my funeral,' he announced.

I politely scoffed at the pressing necessity.

'After the ague which gripped me on Monday night, one must always be ready to stage it. I don't want anything gloomy. All light and joy. Kiri Te Kanawa singing *Tit Willow*, if we can get her.'

Herbert groaned. 'That's been *done*, darling. Funerals as musicals are absolutely *out*.'

Sir Damian reflected, 'Well, they had a pretty long run. I shall have not tears, but laughter. Do you suppose The Two Ronnies would read the lessons?'

'Comics' funerals!' Herbert objected. 'All trotting out their gags to cheer people up. It's like the last cigarette when they're going to shoot you. I don't suppose anyone's really enjoyed it.'

Sir Damian poured himself more champagne.

'I went to a conjurer's funeral once,' he remembered. 'They did tricks. Quite gruesome, particularly as it was a crematorium and the star did the disappearing one as a finale. Perhaps the address could be given by the Minister of Arts, whoever he is?' Sir Damian's face brightened. 'Could we get an Arts Council grant for the whole thing?'

Herbert gulped. 'You're making me quite weepy, duckie. I'd like something simple, just you and me.'

'A village funeral,' Sir Damian pronounced thoughtfully. '*Beneath those rugged elms, that yew-tree's shade* – remember when I read that lovely poem over at the BBC, Herbert? They were dreadfully skinflint about the fee. I quite fancy a plain coffin of English oak borne by yeomen to the lamentations of maidens, but I suppose both are difficult to come by these days. Anyway, the vicar's dreadfully upstage about his churchyard, it's quite as difficult to get into as *No Sex Please, We're British* on a Saturday night.'

He sighed. 'I'll have to end up with everyone else like *rognons flambés*,' he resigned himself.

Herbert reasoned more cheerfully, 'What's the point,

arranging the closing night party when you're still playing to packed houses, sweetie?'

Sir Damian scraped up his omelette. I coughed.

'Oh, the doctor! Kind of you to look in, but I think it came from lying in a draught as Caesar's corpse.'

'My bill,' I recalled firmly.

'I shall settle it here and now.'

'Good!'

'Far better than pay you so trifling a sum, I'll let you in for a grand backing my forthcoming production of *Gammer Gurton's Needle* in modern dress. It made them fall about in the middle of the sixteenth century. Can't fail, despite what everyone in the West End seems to be telling me. You're a lucky man, doctor. Isn't he, Herbert? Meanwhile, here's a couple of stalls for tomorrow night, you can see for yourself how hopelessly wrong the critics were about my current show. Sorry I can't offer you any lunch, but I'm expecting dear Michael and Dulcie any minute to organize the Chichester Festival.'

At the front door, Herbert rubbed his thumb and forefinger.

'The price of the tickets. Though we take credit card bookings, if it helps.'

I drove away deliberating that Nye Bevan was right. Private patients brought only trouble.

41

7

As I went downstairs in my pyjamas to collect Thursday morning's papers from our rustic porch the telephone rang.

It was Walter Elmsworthy.

'Where the hell are you?' I asked.

'Back home.' He seemed offended. 'You surely didn't begrudge me a couple of days' seclusion, in the circumstances?'

'I've been trying to phone you about Annabel Blackadder.'

'Ah! You've already heard?'

'Yes. No. What?'

'She's been arrested.'

'Thank God!' I could not help myself exclaiming. 'I mean, we must be thankful the mystery's solved.'

'She took the carbon of that letter from Mrs Proudfoot's desk.'

'No!'

'The police came for her at six this morning. I've just had her father on the line. Understandably, in a frenzied state.'

'But what was she arrested *for*?'

'Theft. Apparently it applies equally to a sheet of paper as a pile of banknotes. Particularly if someone on high wants it to.'

'She confessed?'

'No. The editor of the paper gave her away.'

'The little faecal specimen! He swore he wouldn't.'

'He did?' There was a pause. 'What do you know about this that I don't?'

'Nothing, nothing,' I told him hastily. 'I must have read it in the papers.'

I hurried upstairs.

'Douglas Blackadder's kid's been nicked for pinching Jim's letter from Walter Elmsworthy's secretary's desk,' I told Sandra breathlessly.

She sat up in bed. 'The little bitch!'

'She was behaving from the highest motives,' I defended Annabel. 'If misguided ones. Like the men who shot Lincoln, Kennedy, Ghandi and the Archduke Ferdinand.'

'But how can you possibly know about her motives?'

'She told me so. In the surgery, a couple of days ago.'

'And you told Jim?' Sandra asked anxiously.

'Of course not. Professional secrecy. I couldn't tell the police. I couldn't even tell you.'

She was horrified. 'But darling! Won't you get into trouble?'

'I could have gone to jail. There'd have been no one to propose the toast at Jilly's wedding.'

She kissed me dramatically. 'Darling! I shall stand by you.'

'Thank you.'

The lens which creates the world for so many of its inhabitants focussed on Annabel. Television at midday showed her scurrying from our magistrates' court with her burly, silver-haired father. Everything happening in Churchford seemed to be news, of a discreditable sort. The inhabitants of Sodom and Gomorrah must have begun to feel the same.

Before evening surgery I drove to the Blackadders. They had a comfortable prewar house with hydrangeas, a tennis court and a privet-fringed front drive, outside which the inquisitors' caravan had shifted from Jim's. I hurried from my car amid clicking shutters and shouted questions – was I relative, lawyer, friend? The front door sprung ajar as I hastened up. I pushed inside, confronted by Douglas Blackadder demanding furiously, 'What have you done to my daughter?'

'What! Me? Nothing.'

'Yes, you have. You've betrayed her confidence. You

43

should be utterly ashamed of yourself.'

'I bloody have not!' I responded, enraged. 'You don't say that to any doctor.' I added, 'Particularly one who makes up a regular foursome.'

'How could Scotland Yard have got her name otherwise?'

I noticed Annabel standing at the foot of the stairs, expressionless.

'You were the only person in the world she trusted with the truth about this . . . this . . . prank,' he said resentfully. 'Oh, God, what a sickening business! At first I didn't think they were going to allow Annabel bail.'

'It was the editor who revealed Annabel's name,' I protested. 'That's what Walter Elmsworthy told me.'

'But the police must have gone to him already armed with it.'

'Why?'

'Because the editor promised solemnly to protect her.'

'If solemnity kept promises, adultery would never have been invented,' I pointed out.

'But a man in such a position . . .' He waved his hand unbelievingly. 'A man responsible for one of our great national newspapers. It's unthinkable he should dishonourably break his word.'

'Rubbish!' I said briskly. 'Anyway, he sees plenty of examples in his own pages every week.'

He persisted, 'Particularly when his informant was of tender years, unaware of the ways of the world, and ignorant that she would be faced with a serious criminal charge.'

'Smelling a serious charge against himself, he would have betrayed Orphan Annie.'

The torrent of Douglas Blackadder's anger slackened with swirls of doubt. 'I suppose anyone tries to save their own skin when confronted by a policeman. Whether they're editing newspapers or selling them.'

Annabel broke her silence. 'It couldn't be Dr Gordon who gave them my name, daddy.'

'Why not?' he asked.

44

'Because he never thought I was wicked about the drugs or the shoplifting or anything. He just said I was a bloody little fool. I knew I could trust him. He'd never land me in trouble. I mean, he said there was enough of the natural sort in the world without having to go round making any more, didn't you?'

This seemed to soften her father. 'Yes, Richard, I know you're a good sort. This devilish letter's brought pain enough to the family. We mustn't let it cause more between ourselves.'

I agreed warmly. 'We must be practical,' I insisted.

'I've already been on to Sir David Napley's firm. They're the best criminal solicitors in London.'

I continued forcefully, 'Annabel must get hold of this lovely MP she met at the party. He's the one who fired the torpedo which turned the leak into a shipwreck. And he gave his word of honour to protect her from any consequences.'

Douglas Blackadder suggested doubtfully, 'Do you think promises keep any better in Westminster than in Fleet Street?'

'He might get his party leader to press for the charge being dropped. A lot of politics is conducted on the backstairs, you know. The grand front ones under the chandeliers are only to impress the humble public shivering outside the front door.'

'But I've been trying.' Annabel sounded panicky. 'His secretary keeps saying he's busy.'

'Tell her he'd better find time to answer the phone,' I directed sternly. 'Or you'll pass the story of his appallingly disgraceful conduct to Jim Whynn, who will have no trouble inserting it tomorrow morning in a pro-Government tabloid. Whether red-nosed or blue-nosed,' I reasoned, 'our politicians like to keep them clean.'

Annabel shuddered. 'I don't want to talk to another newspaper. I don't even want to read one.'

'Then *I'll* handle it,' I said resolutely.

I left. I felt uneasily that all I had accomplished with Douglas Blackadder was convincing him I was a skilful liar.

I signed my statement at the police station. I still did not confess to Annabel's confession. I felt like the little boy in the lovely painting *When Did You Last See Your Father?* telling the Roundheads I was an orphan.

I reached the surgery. Mrs Jenkins tremblingly asked to see me in private. She said she could stand it no longer. After fifteen years, she was leaving on Monday. I shrugged. I felt I was watching the ship's cat follow the departing rats.

I telephoned Jim Whynn's secretary the name of the opposition MP, but the only fresh news in next morning's papers was Annabel's being voted vice-president of the Friends of Man (the boringly self-conscious do-gooders), of Moral Concern (who believed everyone should live as boringly high-minded as themselves), and Meadowsweet (outdoor bores). I sighed over my porridge with skimmed milk. I hoped the poor girl would see they were meaningless medals, awarded only for the colourful publicity of their ribbons.

'None of them would so much as send in a hot lunch to her during the trial adjournment,' I observed sourly to Sandra.

'You *are* becoming a cynic,' she said mildly.

'After this week, I wouldn't buy a secondhand car from John the Baptist.'

'What exactly will happen to the child now?'

'I suppose the Government will exert its right to an Old Bailey trial, and put her in front of what we used to call a reliable hanging judge.'

I was wrong. Annabel was tried in early May by the Churchford magistrates. It was the fate of all other local petty thieves. But the Government sent a forensic sledgehammer to crack a peanut. They dispatched from Whitehall to prosecute the case the Attorney-General himself – the chief law officer of the Crown, a Privy Councillor, the head of the English Bar, the successor in office to Francis Bacon and Lord Birkenhead. It indicated the Government's outrage at the mental instability of its MPs being paraded.

The shoplifting, the drugs, the disorderly demonstrating sounded as felonious footsteps towards the terrible deed. She got six months. Less would have been seen by our well-mannered magistrates as much a discourtesy towards their distinguished visitor as inviting him to an uneatable dinner.

Walter Elmsworthy and myself left the court together.

'What did you think about it?' I asked gloomily.

'I can't think about anything except the relief of being able to reinstate Lynda Proudfoot. Her successor was terrible. Lost everything. I hear your receptionist's leaving *you*?'

Annabel's incarceration freed the case as material for *Mediascope*. That night Jim was interviewed by Heathcoate Bullwhistle, to whom most of the country delegated its political thinking.

Jim was self-assured, charming and unashamed. He deftly shifted to Annabel the indignation which the nation had so enjoyably been expending on himself. What would any viewer think of a teenager who went round stealing their own family's intimate medical reports and selling them to the local newspaper?

He was followed by Annabel's gorgeous opposition MP, who had a pink face, a snub nose and a shower of golden hair and resembled a piglet in straw.

Yes, the papers were perfectly truthful. He knew this young lady Annabel. He had a few minutes' chat with her at some party or other – an MP had to attend so many, it was his duty. He was mystified she had dragged him into the sordid affair. He supposed he was the only politician she knew.

'Would you say,' Heathcoate Bullwhistle glared through his glasses, 'that the girl's action was malicious?'

The MP sighed. 'Were I a private individual – yes, certainly. But a public figure must tolerate being used by wrongdoers who want to save their own necks.'

I extinguished his expression of sorrowful selflessness.

'If ever that man hears a cock crow, he should die of shame,' I announced to Sandra.

The hand which poured the Glenmorangie trembled. I recalled glumly a remark by Claude Cockburn, the wittiest man ever employed by the *Daily Worker* – 'But then a cat's-paw is a cat's-paw and must expect to be treated as part of the cat.'

Poor Annabel. She had no claws.

It was the saddest of cases because everyone had been behaving normally – according to their lights.

Though my own lights did not always shine unmurkily . . .

8

'*Torschlusspanik!*' I exclaimed. 'That's the word I was searching for.'

'What dear?' asked Sandra over her muesli, the food for constipated parrots.

'*Torschlusspanik!*' I repeated.

I rose from the breakfast table in our sunlit Victorian kitchen and glared through the window into the burgeoning back garden.

'And what does *that* mean?' she enquired, smiling over Fred Bassett.

'Terror as the doors are about to shut. In German, they being profound thinkers.'

'What doors?' she asked absently.

'Of life.'

She murmured, 'Oh, if you're near the High Street, can you pick up some redcurrant jelly?'

I sighed. 'Now my arteries are hardening, my cataracts thickening, my brain softening – and I really *must* get Jilly to fix something for my varicose veins at the General – I ask, What have I done in my entire existence? What am I doing?'

Sandra sighed deeply. 'I *do* wish Jilly and Peter would decide on their wedding day. It's like having an unexploded bomb in my social life.'

I continued tragically, 'I can no longer keep up with the latest in medicine. Not to mention the latest health lunacies. That rude woman Charlotte Whynn was right. I'm old-fashioned. A GP can get away with being pretty thick, but it doesn't take much intelligence to be deeply caring and committed. What do I do? Distribute scripts for Valium like a bank clerk fivers. I'm bored.'

Sandra became suddenly aware that my soul was in torment.

'You gloomy old thing, you! This lovely May morning.'

'Bloody spring!' I muttered savagely. 'The seasons are starting to change quicker than the programmes on the telly. It always seems to be Christmas. How few more springs,' I demanded, 'before I am enjoying a backseat ride with Francis Chappell and Sons?'

She indicated the bright side. 'You've got your snooker.'

'Snooker!' I pronounced doomfully.

Belatedly disturbed by my miserable mien, Sandra threw aside the newspaper and stood up.

'Richard darling! Just count your blessings. You've a lovely home. A lovely family. A lovely wife.'

I agreed with all three.

'And even the Cheshire Cat would look miserable after that awful month you had with Jim Whynn and poor little Annabel.'

'Bloody Quaggy!' I growled contemptuously.

'Kiss me,' said Sandra. 'No! Not like that. Like when we were married. That's right.'

I felt like Judas gently nibbling the lobe of Jesus' ear.

I arrived for morning surgery. Mrs Jenkins' temporary replacement was already busy in my consulting room.

'Good morning, doctor.'

'Good morning, Mrs Osgood.'

'Would you care for your coffee now, or later, doctor?'

'A little later, I fancy.'

'Exactly as you wish, doctor. I've arranged all your patients' cards, in the correct order.'

'Thank you, Mrs Osgood.'

'Not at all, doctor. First is Mrs Days, with the drink problem.'

I sighed. 'There's a lot of it about.'

'Indeed, doctor.' She hesitated. 'I never told you, did I? My ex-husband was an aggressive alcoholic psychopath.'

'No! The swine.'

50

Mrs Osgood had a trick of dropping her eyes as she spoke. She had a husky voice. She was slim, calm, gentle and graceful. She resembled a Renaissance Madonna with smashing tits.

She was the same age as my daughter Jilly.

'Oh, I feel no rancour about it,' she continued softly. 'Good can come from these terrible mistakes, can't it? If you trouble yourself to search for it. One day I must tell you the whole story of my divorce, doctor.'

'Please. Any time. I shall be all ears.'

'Despite all the pain, I realized that my husband was sick rather than evil. The experience left me with an urge to help others who might be suffering worse troubles.'

'Which you do so delightfully, Mrs Osgood.'

'Thank you, doctor. Of course, my husband had been married twice before.'

'Really? You poor little thing, Mrs Osgood.'

'Perhaps that was his appeal. It's funny, but I always seem to go for the older man.'

She raised her eyes and stared at me.

I said urk.

'I've brought a tin of chocolate biscuits, doctor. You must have one with your coffee.'

'That would be lovely, Mrs Osgood.'

She patted my hand. 'You need looking after, doctor.'

She left. Her legs were as shapely as hock bottles.

I sat staring at Mrs Day's card.

In the fortnight since her arrival, Mrs Osgood had been flashing more green lights than British Rail. A thought tortured me – terrible, tantalizing, thrilling, tasty. Her every glance carried RSVP. Should I be delighted to accept her kind invitation?

I was a good husband, a respected father, an alabaster figure in the local statuary. And God knows what they would have thought at the golf club.

I reflected sombrely on what we doctors call the endocrine orchestra. The scatterd glands whose harmonious hormones call the tune of love, after some years' tuning-up sound the rousing overtures of puberty, play the passionate symphonies of youth, provide the programme music of middle life and render the laments of age. I wondered if Mrs Osgood embodied the last chance before mine struck up *The Last Post*.

'*Torschlusspanik!*' I exclaimed, frightening the patient.

Over the coffee and chocolate biscuit I remarked, 'Mrs Osgood, would you like this job permanently?'

'Oh, doctor!' she said huskily. 'I'm thrilled you should ask. May I think about it?' She dropped her eyes. 'There is someone else in my life to consider.'

I gasped. 'Another man?'

She stared at me. 'Oh, no, doctor. I haven't found the right one, I'm afraid. They all seem so juvenile, so callow, so empty-headed these days. Mrs Whynn phoned. Would you call to see her husband? He has a temperature.'

My eyebrows rose. 'But they're Dr Quaggy's patients . . .'

I rubbed my hands.

One of the foreign girls opened the oast house door and led me to the white circular bedroom over the living room. Jim was sitting up in a four-poster with all the morning's papers over the embroidered coverlet. He was flushed and reading a White Paper. I was glad to find Charlotte gone out. I was not certain we had yet buried the meat knife.

'Summer flu,' I pronounced, removing the thermometer. 'There's a lot of it about.'

'I could put up with combined smallpox, cholera and leprosy,' he observed cheerfully. 'The Minister I worked for has got the sack. It'll be all over Monday's papers. The Prime Minister's been itching to get rid of the incompetent braggart for months, but was frustrated by his powerful friends. They could have caused endless trouble from the back benches. But now my opinions are known to every man, woman and child who watches television, his friends have decided to desert him.'

'They agree with you?'

'Not in the least. They see his reputation's gone through

the shredder, and it's wiser to keep clear of him. Failure's more catching than flu. And the PM's so delighted at the chance to appear a tough, resolute, national leader dedicated to efficiency, it's been hinted that I'm so entirely forgiven my political career can resume in a few months. Which was exactly what the doctor ordered,' he ended delightedly.

'Stay in bed for a couple of days and take plenty of fluids.'

Jim was not heeding.

'Meanwhile, I must keep my name in front of the electorate with some good controversial local issues. I'll ask my opponent to a meal. I expect we can fix some tussle to our mutual advantage. Though most of his hobby-horses are admittedly non-starters.'

I was surprised. 'You're on dining terms with Bert Bullivant?'

'Heavens, yes. We were at Balliol together. We played in the same pop group. He was Bertie then.'

I cocked my head admiringly. 'Aren't we a cleverer country than we care to claim, conducting such civilized politics?'

He laughed. 'On the contrary – Beatrice Webb was an unusually perceptive socialist when she said, "We are all of us good natured and stupid folk. The worst of it is that the governing classes are as good natured and stupid as the Labour movement." '

I snapped my bag shut. 'I needn't see you again. Congratulations on the resumption of progress towards prime minister.'

He said thoughtfully, 'It was a pity about that stupid girl. And her father having to resign from the golf club. She should have stuck out for trial by jury at the Old Bailey. I expect they would have acquitted her. The limitless suspicion of governments by juries is one of the glories of the British Constitution.'

'She's in an open prison in Essex,' I informed him.

'Those places aren't too bad, they tell me.'

'They're terrible. Bread-and-marge and boredom. Lavatory-cleaning and lesbianism.' I hesitated. 'You preferred me to Dr Quaggy after all?'

'We felt it fortunate to have a family friend who happened to be a doctor,' he told me simply. 'And I felt I'd been rather unjust, holding you responsible for an obnoxious little bit of sneak-thieving.'

'That makes what I have to say both easier and harder. Could you do something for Annabel when she's released?'

Jim looked startled.

I added hastily, 'She'd easily get a job with some loony organization like Women for Life. But she needs to start the normal dull existence that most adults are lucky to enjoy. Could you . . . well, say something in the local paper that now she'd been punished you forgave her?'

He started coughing. 'This damn sore throat. Should I gargle?'

'A nice taste and a nice noise, but useless.'

'You doctors do strip illness of its little pleasures.'

'How about Annabel?'

He blew his nose loudly. 'In victory, magnanimity. To quote Churchill again. Very well. Remind me.'

I thanked him warmly. 'How are the bowels?'

'Fine. What's Dr Barty-Howells like?'

'You don't want a second opinion on flu, surely?'

'His name came up at Westminster. As one of my constituents. He's among the consultant physicians at the Churchford General Hospital, I believe?'

'Everyone says he's absolutely brilliant,' I assured him.

Basil Barty-Howells was one of the intense, effective, uninteresting sort, of whom people found absolutely nothing else to say.

'He's very big in the environment.'

I nodded. 'Which in my young days was called the open air.'

'Also acid rain and clubbed seals, I understand. Newts, too.'

'And squashed toads on motorways.'

'A friend?'

'He calls often. He believes strongly in consultants cooperating with GPs. I think he regards us as another endangered lovable species requiring protection.'

'You needn't mention I asked of him,' Jim remarked mysteriously. 'Thank you for coming so quickly, Richard. Did I hear you're retiring?'

'Retire? Me? Nonsense!' I stared, shocked. 'I'm still quite a young dog yet, you know.'

'*Torschlusspanik!*' I was saying that evening to Jack Windrush, the pathologist at the General with the medical student sense of humour. 'Do you know what that means?'

I potted a red.

He chalked his cue. 'Let's work it out – fear of the dark after losing your torch?'

I shook my head. '*Tor*, door. *Schluss*, shutting. *Panik*, panic.'

I potted brown.

The new snooker table at the golf club fascinated me. Snooker was my only distinction as a student at St Swithin's. I was sad to give it up as a busy GP. I played three times a week with Jack, a tall, sinewy man and captain of the Churchford XI, who conceded that snooker enjoyed estimable similarities to cricket – both games were played on smooth, level, restful green by men in shirt-sleeves bashing hard balls about with bits of wood, snooker having the advantage that rain never stopped play and naked idiots had not yet been seen on television invading the pitch.

Sandra did not seem to mind being left alone in Foxglove Lane. She said it cheered a man up, discovering in middle age he had not lost the touch for something he was performing every night in his youth.

Jack Windrush was puzzled. 'You mean, it's some phobia that grips nervous Tube passengers?'

I potted a red. I was in exhilarated mood.

'It means a fright at last chance time. The Germans have a

fondness for expressing the obvious philosophically.'

'Sexual, I suppose?' he enquired.

'Funny you should suggest that. I had a case only today. A mature gent who was worried whether an affair he was seriously contemplating with a younger woman would be consummated only by him looking a ridiculous fool.'

I potted green.

'How mature?'

'Oh, round my age.'

Jack guffawed. 'Any woman remotely near your age would already be impeccably past the menopause.'

I missed a red.

'*Torschlusspanik!*' Jack repeated thoughtfully. 'It recalls the classical definition – fear is the first time you find you can't do it twice, panic the second you can't do it once.'

He potted a red, and added, 'Perhaps the term applies to the woman who wanted a hysterectomy because she was afraid of having more grandchildren?'

He missed the black.

'I treated Jim Whynn today for this flu which everyone's got.'

'I'm sure that fuss did him no harm. It was all much more fun than a party political broadcast.'

I lined up my shot.

'At first he thought about me much as the Government do about the Russian spies they keep employing with such depressing regularity in our secret service. But he decided against putting himself in the hands of Quaggy, one of medicine's most unpleasant side-effects.'

I potted a red.

'He was tactfully sounding me out about Basil Barty-Howells,' I revealed.

'Now, Basil's been behaving very peculiarly recently,' Jack imparted. 'I decided he was cracking under the strain of educating the local GPs. Are you going to his lecture at the General on Friday week? It's on electrolyte balance. Can't imagine anything more boring except the sex life of whales, which he's so bothered about. God! You nearly tore the cloth.'

A thought had put me off my stroke. On Friday week I should ask Mrs Osgood to dinner by candlelight, available at the Old Tyme Inne, five miles along the Dover road.

9

The following evening, Basil Barty-Howells appeared unexpectedly at my house in Foxglove Lane.

He was a tall, youngish-looking, curly, craggy man, with a neat goatee beard, pale blue eyes and hairy suits. He ate a lot of bran.

It was a May evening, warm enough to sit on the flag-stoned terrace against the back lawn. He knocked back three swift Glenlivets, which was strange. The usual Barty-Howells social call involved twiddling a small glass of Tio Pepe and a discussion on neurophysiology, which was as boring as electrolyte balance.

Suddenly he looked round furtively.

'Where's Sandra?'

'In the kitchen.'

'Richard! Can you keep a deadly secret?'

I was alarmed.

Basil Barty-Howells could be infuriating in his complacent, unsweated intelligence, but he was a pleasant colleague, a kindly and conscientious Churchford citizen. Had he suffered some moral lapse? Confused the consulting room with the bedroom?

I said, 'Cross my heart, or I die.'

His glance quivered searchingly round the laurel hedges and rose beds.

'On the third Saturday in June they're going to give me a knighthood. In the morning. It's the Queen's birthday.'

I congratulated him.

He added nervously, 'I'm afraid it's going to cause a lot of local jealousy.'

I said soothingly, 'My dear Basil, that's inescapable. All knighthoods create jealousy, even the deserved ones.'

'I mean among the local doctors.'

'Oh, I fancy all doctors are familiar with the professional tariff. Sirs for Presidents of the Royal Colleges of Surgery and so forth. Otherwise, medical honours are only a matter of killing the right people. Regicide is always good for a peerage.'

He fixed me with his pale blue eyes. 'How many times must you have scanned the Honours List and exclaimed, Not *him!*'

'Haven't read it for years. Grown impatient of all dull reading matter.'

He shook his head wildly.

'You see, Richard, I'm not getting it for my clinical work among patients. Frankly, at a dump like the Churchford General, you'd as much expect to collect a knighthood for service to medicine as a Cup Winners' medal playing for a side in the Fourth Division, for God's sake include that in your oath of secrecy.'

'You're getting it for your work on acid rain, clubbed seals and newts. Also flattened toads.'

He looked amazed.

'How did you know? Of course, I'm also into gassed badgers, whales of all sorts and recently child poverty.'

Basil Barty-Howells operated at the treetop of Meadowsweet, the society deeply concerned about All things bright and beautiful, All creatures great and small. Vegetation and wildlife seemed harmless enough items to make their agitators feel significant. Jim Whynn's diagnosis was shrewd. Pressure groups have a few at the top who confuse the importance of human or animal life with their own, a few at the bottom behaving as aggressively as they are naturally inclined with a clear conscience, and a bored mass in between as squeezed of individuality by the machinery of modern government as oranges in a juice factory.

'Of course, I've sat on endless government committees, wasted a vast amount of time I should have been giving to my patients, but I suppose it was all worthwhile to achieve

59

. . . well, leadless petrol some time in the future and a few plugged radiation leaks.'

He looked as miserable as a toad in heavy traffic.

'Will you believe me, Richard, I accepted the honour without a second thought? It seemed something you didn't need to argue about, like getting the good conduct prize at school. Now I've honestly developed profound doubts about my worthiness. And I can hardly bite the hand that bestows the accolade, can I?'

I assured him warmly that everyone knew him to be Churchford's answer to Mother Teresa of Calcutta (who I had only recently discovered not to be a literary creation of Malcolm Muggeridge's).

Basil Barty-Howells sighed deeply. 'You've been a great help, Richard. You know, you're the only man in the whole world I'd trust with the secret.'

I was so flattered I invited him to dinner on Saturday. At snooker that evening I invited the Windrushes too.

Jack and Daphne Windrush arrived first.

'I don't think I've ever seen such a change in a chap as in Barty-Howells these last few weeks,' Jack reiterated over his first Laphroaig. 'When he wasn't busy letting us know how clever he was, old Basil was as placid as a well-heeled farmer in muck. Suddenly he's become as jumpy as a flea circus.'

'Strange,' I remarked. 'Very, very strange.'

Jack looked round the room shiftily.

'I happen to know why,' he whispered to Sandra and myself.

I looked blank.

'On the Queen's Birthday he's getting a handle.'

'No!'

'He confided in me,' Jack revealed proudly.

'And he absolutely hates the idea.'

Jack looked shocked. 'How did you know?'

'Because he confided in me, too.'

Jack sniffed. 'Well, I rather suspect he's secretly told the entire staff of the General.'

'Perhaps it was predictable?' I suggested. 'Some men have the stamp of knighthood from youth, as others you know are going to go bald.'

'When you accept these things,' Sandra suggested, 'can't you opt for no publicity, like winning the pools?'

We were interrupted by the arrival of Basil Barty-Howells and his wife Margaret, a beefy, blonde physiotherapist he met while jogging – he was inevitably also a fitness nut. I often spotted them in Churchford's avenues in matching tracksuits, pink and panting, open-mouthed and glassy-eyed, a faintly indecent conjugation.

Margaret usually chirped across the dinner table about washing machine programmes, deep-freezing fruit and worming the dog, the periscope of her mind not protruding far above the domestic parapets. Now she declared shrilly over the avocados with prawns, 'Don't you think that Churchford is really most frightfully, frightfully dull?'

I disagreed, with mention of the archaeology exhibition at the public library.

'I've told Basil that we absolutely must go to live in London – Chelsea, Kensington, Knightsbridge or somewhere, so convenient for Harrods.'

She was suddenly excited, only a glass of supermarket Muscadet, too.

'One gets in such a rut here,' she confessed. 'Next year we really must make an effort to get about – you know, Ascot, Covent Garden, Glyndebourne, Cowes.'

'Cruft's?' suggested Jack.

'I want to make a lot of exciting new friends,' she revealed, throwing both hands in the air.

Basil looked sneakily round the table and muttered, 'It won't make any difference to our way of life.'

'What won't?' Jack asked at once.

'Winning *The Times* Portfolio game,' he replied.

He headed the conversation into neurophysiology for the rest of the evening, which was so boring I had to open another bottle of Laphroaig.

Basil and I were alone in the hall as Margaret demanded the loo before leaving.

He gripped my elbow. 'I can't go on any longer. A dozen times I've reached for the phone to tell the Palace I've scratched.'

'Cheer up!' I urged. 'It'll be all over once the Queen's had her birthday. You can do a lap of honour round the General, then everyone will forget you've got it. Don't you remember – it took about twenty-four hours, after that you didn't think twice about everybody suddenly calling you "Doctor".'

His eye brightened, but he added anxiously, 'You haven't told a soul?'

I shook my head vigorously.

'People are starting to suspect,' he imparted hoarsely. 'They're saying twee things to Margaret, like when she was having a baby. Coming to my lecture on electrolyte balance on Friday?' he changed the subject as she appeared.

'I'd love to. It sounds dreadfully interesting. But I'm worked off my feet at the moment. Summer flu, you know,' I apologized.

As we shut the front door Sandra asked, 'And whose birthday is it in June, then?'

I told her, 'The Queen's.'

'And what about mine?' I noticed her lip trembling. 'It's the day before. And it's a special one.'

'Oh? Really? Is it?' I was lost. 'How old are you?'

'Honestly!' she said furiously. 'I'd expect a doctor at least to remember how old people are.'

'With the patients, it's written on their cards,' I pointed out.

'I'm asking my brother George and his wife for a few days.'

'Not that awful couple!' I cried.

'I just can't understand why you create so much. My brother George is utterly delightful company. Everyone says what a scream he is. And Dilys can hardly help that tic. Further, if you get pissed all the time, like you did when they

62

came for Christmas, I shall leave you and you'll have to iron your own shirts.'

She went upstairs and slammed the bedroom door.

Remorse tore at me like dyspepsia. I was no saint. I tried only to be a good sort. Which most saints, being prickly personalities, probably were not. On Friday I was to enjoy an illicit dinner with Mrs Osgood, by candlelight. I felt so ashamed I went into the kitchen and did all the washing-up.

Thursday. I came home from evening surgery to find Basil Barty-Howells agitatedly pacing my sitting room.

I was shocked at his degeneration over the week. He was pale, haggard, shaky, and swiftly downed a couple of Dal-whinnies before revealing, 'In strictest confidence, Richard, something terrible has happened. You know I had a first wife, Lynn, in Pinner?'

I murmured tactfully that I had heard something of it.

'Also a little boy, Fabian.'

Sprawled in an armchair, he suddenly had a dreamy look.

'Lynn and I were militant young socialists. All for the brotherhood of man and soak the rich. I had a much bigger beard in those days.'

He sighed. 'How simple the world looks through starry eyes! I felt that I must inform her of the approaching honour.' He vindicated himself, 'After all, we have mingled our genes.'

'And she was utterly disgusted,' I supplied. 'She's refusing you access to the child.'

'On the contrary, she's been going round Pinner calling herself Lady Barty-Howells since Bank Holiday Monday. I drove over yesterday and confronted her,' he explained distraughtly. 'I explained that the title goes only to the current incumbent. Like . . . well . . . a personalized number plate, which you transfer from some old banger to the new model. But she didn't seem to follow the argument.'

I consoled him. 'After all, it's not a criminal offence impersonating a lady. Not like a policewoman.'

He said agitatedly, 'But the silly bitch, jumping the gun like that! Doubtless MI5 operates in Pinner? Why, the intelligence is probably already in the Prime Minister's ears, the Queen's, too. What's the penalty for a breach of security over government hand-outs? Look at the turmoil over Jim Whynn. Instant cancellation, I'm certain.'

I said, 'Well, that would make your mind up for you, wouldn't it?'

He cried miserably, 'But I can't get out of it. My wife would leave me.'

'And you'd have to iron your own shirts?'

'That's right!'

I invited him to Sandra's birthday party.

Friday morning.

'What's wrong with you?' Sandra asked irritably at breakfast. 'The way you're fidgeting, you could be developing the alcoholic shakes.'

I explained vaguely, 'It's Basil Barty-Howells. His nerves seem to have infected me.'

'What a stupid man he is,' Sandra decided. 'You can look a gift horse in the mouth, but you shouldn't let it give you a painful bite. Are you really going to stir your coffee with your toast?'

'*Torschlusspanik!*' I murmured uneasily.

Basil Barty-Howells was waiting at my surgery.

'Something worse has happened.' He paced my small consulting room. 'You're the only one I can tell, Richard. My first wife's turned up.'

'From Pinner?'

He shook his head impatiently.

'The Pinner one's my second, actually. Nobody in Churchford knows about the one in Streatham. I married at eighteen. Before I was even a medical student. Great mistake. Sex, you know. I was naïve. She instructed me. I didn't know till later she was running a sexual driving school. Now she wants to be introduced to all my friends as the girl who could have been Lady Barty-Howells. She's changed.

Haven't we all? She's fat and florid. She's appeared this morning in Churchford.'

He smiled unexpectedly. 'I've always had a soft spot for my first bedmate. I think all men do, if they can remember them. She was a fish-fryer. She won't do my private practice much good in a place like this.'

I exclaimed, 'But how could she have heard of your impending elevation?'

He shrugged. 'I come from an ordinary working-class family, you know. I slipped in the hyphen when I grew the beard. We all create an image, don't we? What a dull place the world would be if we were all ourselves! I had to tell my mum and dad. They were pretty thrilled, you can imagine. So much so, they passed it on to the kin. Even utmost cousins. I've already had congratulations from New Zealand. Also, some of my family are saying that now I'm a knight I must be stinking rich, and a loan would come in handy.'

He looked evasive. 'I've an uncle who's a bit of a crook. Oh, quite a respectable one. Embezzlement. He most unhappily had to go inside once or twice. Obviously I'm not enthusiastic about having him in Churchford. Particularly talking to the *Churchford Echo*. Which he's threatening to do, in default of a few hundred quid by the Queen's Birthday. It's all a terrible strain. I'm cancelling my lecture tonight.'

I jumped from my chair. 'Don't do that!'

He looked puzzled. 'But you're not going.'

'Lots of other GPs have been looking forward to it enormously. They have been talking of little else for weeks. You're the only one to do anything about the appalling ignorance that the other consultants imply as a matter of course we wallow in.'

'All right, all right . . . I suppose if it's my duty.'

He had to hurry for a clinic at the General. Mrs Osgood appeared with the first patients' cards.

'Tonight, Mrs Osgood,' I murmured.

She dropped her eyes. 'How could I forget, doctor?'

'We can go straight from evening surgery.'
'Oh no! I've got a lovely new dress at home.'
'*Torschlusspanik!*' I muttered, licking my lips.

10

The Old Tyme Inne was 1930s Tudor, a 'roadhouse', an ancient monument from the era when driving a car was as romantic as flying your own plane.

The food was choking. The wine was poisonous. The waiters were unintelligible.

The evening was delicious.

And the candlelight was as good as you would get anywhere.

'You really are the most wonderful person I've ever met, doctor,' said Mrs Osgood huskily, dropping her eyes over her coffee with *crème de menthe* and After Eight.

I said tut.

'So helpful,' she breathed. 'So kind. So considerate.'

I said tut tut.

'So understanding, so gentle, so courteous, so chivalrous.'

I said tut tut tut.

Mrs Osgood sighed deeply.

'I never imagined, after that perfectly disgusting divorce, that I'd find . . .' Her eyes held mine. 'Such a lovely boss.'

I asked pressingly, 'Not pompous?'

'Oh, no, doctor! Your conversation twinkles like bubbles in a glass.'

I held her hand across the paper marigolds.

'Mrs Osgood,' I suggested modestly. 'You are so refreshing you must find parts of me which other people cannot reach.'

She left her hand *in situ*. She dropped her eyes. She said huskily, 'Oh, I do, I do, doctor.'

I added another hand to her hand.

'I'd love you to come to my flat, doctor,' she murmured.

I jumped up. 'Now?'

'Oh, no.' She seemed surprised. 'Not at this moment.'

I gathered the scattered marigolds.

'When, Mrs Osgood?' I implored.

She nibbled her After Eight. 'Perhaps after the weekend, doctor?'

'Fine!' I exclaimed. I sat down again. 'Monday? Tuesday?'

'Wednesday?'

'Lovely!'

She smiled slowly. 'There! You are so nice. You didn't need inviting twice.'

'What a delightful modesty you display about your overwhelming sexual attraction,' I meant to say, but it came out urk.

Her eyes dropped as beautifully as butterflies alighting on roses.

'Come early after surgery, doctor. We can make a night of it.'

'Splendid!' I cried. I gathered up the marigolds again.

I arrived home towards midnight. I had qualms. But even Mr Pickwick had his amorous adventures. He found himself in the bedroom of the middle-aged lady in the yellow curl-papers at the Great White Horse in Ipswich. He was looking for his watch. A likely story!

I softly opened the front door. The lights were still on. I was surprised. Sandra was sitting beside the hearth, embroidering a tea cosy.

I said jovially, 'Staying up late, dear?'

'It was a long lecture at the General?'

'Dreadfully. Hours and hours. You know Basil Barty-Howells. Absolutely brilliant, of course, electrolyte balance at his finger tips, but as wordy as an unheckled politician.' I added with satisfaction, 'However, now I know absolutely everything about electrolyte balance.'

I poured myself an Old Fettercairn.

'Since when were you an electrolyte balance buff?' enquired Sandra, stitching.

'Oh, years. Fascinating corner of medicine, electrolyte balance.'

'Come to think of it, when did you last attend a lecture on anything, since you were in medical school and had to?'

'One has the urge,' I enlightened her. 'One must grasp the latest advances before it's too late. *Torschlusspanik!* You know.'

I took a gulp.

'It's a funny thing,' she observed quietly, snipping a stitch. 'That your own partner Elaine Spondek didn't see you there.'

'What the bloody hell was Elaine doing at an electrolyte balance lecture?' I demanded hotly. 'That stuff's far above her head.'

Sandra concentrated on threading a needle. 'She thought it would be a nice gesture towards Basil Barty-Howells.'

I silently poured myself another Old Fettercairn.

'Darling!' Sandra looked at me. 'I'm not cross. Not a little bit.'

'I'm sorry,' I mumbled humbly. 'Dreadfully, dreadfully sorry.'

'You enjoyed yourself?'

I shrugged. 'Not at all. How could I? I was laden with disgrace, remorse, shame.'

She smiled wanly. 'I'm sure you did, really. Didn't you?'

'Perhaps it wasn't too bad,' I admitted.

'There!'

'I deserve absolutely anything you say to me.'

'But I'm touched! You took such trouble, cooking up an excuse.'

'I'm a duplicitous worm,' I conceded.

'Because you know how terribly upset I am at your leaving me alone night after night to go out and play that damfool game snooker.'

She set aside her sewing things. 'I hope you won, darling? Coming to bed?'

I stared after her. I poured myself another Old Fettercairn.

Monday morning.

'What amazing tenderness!' laughed Sandra.

I looked puzzled.

'Richard, you've been biting my ear lobes steadily all
weekend, and now you're boiling me an egg. Is it another
woman? Oh, dear! You've dropped the toast butter side
down. An affair's the usual cause of an unexpected outbreak
of affection in a mature marriage,' she informed me. 'Everyone says so.'

I murmured something unconvincing about redeeming
forgetfulness of her birthday.

My partner motherly Elaine Spondek greeted me in the
small, square, mustard-walled, plastic-floored hall of our
surgery.

'Sandra seemed to think you were attending that horribly
boring lecture on Friday,' she announced cheerfully.

'Can't think what gave her the idea. It was keen of you to
go.'

'Only because I'm hoping that Basil Barty-Howells is
going to buy my old car. I want to talk to you about Judy
Osgood.'

I jumped. 'You mean, the Old Tyme Inne?'

She frowned.

I asked falteringly, 'You know all about it?'

'Well, it's in Yellow Pages.'

'Ah! Then you don't.'

She stared at me. 'Richard, are you suffering from a
confusional state?'

'It's the *Torschlusspanik!*' I explained hastily.

'I do hope you know how to treat it. Listen, I was going to
ask about Judy Osgood.'

I slapped my hands. 'We are just good friends.'

'I should hope so! You're working together all day long.'

'But not that good friends.'

She pursed her lips.

70

'Richard, this is Monday morning, when even the Marx Brothers with performing seals on ice would not be so funny.' She said as to a difficult child, 'I only want to know your assessment of Judy Osgood.'

'A treasure.'

'If she wants to stay, do you want to keep her?'

'I'd love to keep her.'

'That's all right, then. I can't understand your making such a fuss. What was the name of that German disease again?'

'*Torschlusspanik!* There's a lot of it about.'

I strode into my consulting room. Mrs Osgood was laying patient's cards on the desk.

'Har!' I greeted her.

She dropped her eyes.

'Last night was utterly wonderful, doctor.'

'Har!'

'I shall always remember it, doctor.'

'But it won't be anything compared to next Wednesday night.'

She looked up, fluttering her lashes, smiling coyly. 'I'll do my best,' she promised.

'Then you're not going to forget that one, either.'

I rattled cheerfully through my patients.

I ended the morning hoping I had given them all the appropriate prescriptions. Though I suppose with most patients a GP sees, it does not much matter.

'*No* snooker with Jack Windrush this evening,' Sandra reproved me at lunch. 'Have you forgotten that Jilly and Peter are coming for dinner? They've still no more idea of their wedding day than the end of the world.'

I suppose I should have been proud of regular humiliation by someone as brainy as Peter pretending I knew more medicine than he did. Over the roast leg of pork I asked about the latest in gynaecological research.

'Oh, even more dangers in sex,' he replied, smiling. 'We've been through the statistics of men dying from

71

coronaries in bed, and discovered that a high proportion occurred during intercourse.'

'Tut,' I said.

'How dreadful for the poor wife,' observed Jilly.

Peter laughed. 'Be your age, darling. It's generally *not* the poor wife. Most deaths occur during extramarital sex. The excitement, you know.'

'Yes, the excitement,' I muttered.

'I suppose it puts up the blood pressure far higher than the mundane marital sort?' enquired Jilly. 'Mum, you haven't lost your touch with the apple sauce.'

'A squeeze of orange-juice, darling.'

Peter continued informatively, 'Let's take a typical case. Some middle-aged professional or businessman with his twenty-year-old secretary. Probably overweight and under-exercised, blood pressure already a bit up, gets breathless running for a cab. He throws himself into it like trying to win the 100 metres in the Olympics, not a care in the world, then zingo.'

'Horribly embarrassing for the corpse,' Jilly remarked. 'He never knows where he might be found.'

I stared at Peter. 'Rare cases, surely?'

'Really quite frequent, Richard, you'd be surprised. A nasty experience for the girl. I suppose it's like being rolled on by your dead mount in the Grand National.'

'Is your pork all right?' Sandra asked me anxiously.

'I'm not very hungry.'

Wednesday.

I arrived home from evening surgery.

'Darling, I must dash,' I apologized to Sandra. 'I've got Monday's postponed snooker game with Jack Windrush.'

She looked up from arranging a bowl of roses.

'Oh, Jack just rang. Reminding you that if you happened to be thinking of going to the club tonight, the snooker table's booked for the match against the cricket club. Stay at home, dear, and I'll cook you a nice dinner.' She stared at me. 'But what's the matter? It isn't a disaster.'

'I must go out,' I muttered.

She looked concerned. 'Not another attack of that foreign thing, is it?'

'Must go and see some patients,' I croaked.

'But you're not on call, darling! Elaine is.'

'Still must see some patients.'

'You've been seeing patients all day.'

'Must see some more.'

'Surely you can't have any of today's left?'

'Well, I'm going out,' I said.

I went.

Mrs Osgood's flat was in a ten-storey modern block overlooking the Churchill Memorial Park. I had three patients there. I hoped they were out.

I went up in the lift. I had racing pulse, short breath, nausea and dryness of the mouth. The onset of a heart attack? I saw myself coming down again on a stretcher, transported with flashing blue lights to the coronary care unit at the General, and faced with Basil Barty-Howells, who I knew to be as unreliable in the practice of medicine that evening as I was.

I rang the bell. I decided they were all symptoms of *Torschlusspanik!*

Mrs Osgood, radiant in wispy dress.

She gave a lovely smile.

'Hello, doctor,' she said huskily, dropping her eyes. 'This is the moment I've been waiting for.'

I said urk.

'Receiving you in my own home. Do come in.'

I went in.

I could not decide whether I was going to enjoy myself or drop dead.

'You must meet my mother,' said Mrs Osgood.

A good-looking, smartly-dressed, curly-haired lady held out a delicate hand, also with a lovely smile.

'My daughter's told me all about you, doctor.'

I said urk again.

'Thank you so much for looking after Judy. Her life was utterly shattered after that cruel divorce, but she very sensibly didn't want to start rebuilding it the wrong way. Did you, dear? But from all the encouraging things you've said to her in the practice, she's absolutely convinced she's the right type to join.'

'Join what?' I muttered.

'The Samaritans,' said Mrs Osgood proudly. 'Then I can *really* help unfortunate people. Of course it's voluntary, but I've been offered this wonderfully well paid job at the estate agents and I'm starting on Monday. I'm sure you'll overlook the short notice, doctor.' She turned to her mother. 'He's such a good sort.'

Clang!

The *Tor* was *schlussed*.

'You're soon back.' Sandra looked up in surprise from making an omelette. 'You couldn't have seen many patients.'

I poured myself half a tumbler of Genmorangie.

'I haven't seen any patients,' I confessed.

'You left the house as though the Black Death had broken out again.'

'I've been to the Old Tyme Inne. You know, five miles along the Dover Road.'

'But what for? Have you gone off my cooking?'

I drank Glenmorangie and nibbled her earlobe. 'It's as tasty as ever, but you deserve an evening off. On your birthday. I'm standing dinner for fifty. George, Dilys, ask all your family, all our friends in Churchford. It'll be by candle-light.'

'Richard!' She glowed. 'You really are a wonderful husband.'

'Thank you. Also, I've given up snooker.'

That Friday evening, Jack Windrush was the first to arrive at the Old Tyme Inne.

'Sorry I'm early,' he apologized. 'But I thought Daphne could join me here, as I was called urgently to the General. Had to organize a full blood count for Basil Barty-Howells.'

'But he's coming to the dinner party,' I objected.

'He isn't,' said Jack with relish. 'He's going to the theatre with a perforated duodenal ulcer. Jilly says she'll be late, as she's assisting Bill Igtham with the cutting. Though personally, I think Bill's made the wrong diagnosis. It's labour pains, giving birth to a knight. Do I see a bottle of Bruichladdich you've craftily hidden for yourself behind the gladioli? No need to wait for your other guests, surely? Wouldn't it be bloody funny if it comes out at midnight that the Queen has changed her mind about Basil? I hear Margaret's been seen in Asprey's trying on tiaras.'

11

'Nice to be back,' said Mrs Jenkins.

It was early in July. The weather was wonderful. All my patients were damp to the touch.

'That Mrs Osgood.' Mrs Jenkins wrinkled her nose. She was small, dark and fiery. 'She left everything in an unbelievable mess.'

Sitting in my consulting room chair, I groaned. 'I rather let her get on with things herself. Hardly exchanged a word with her from one day to another. She seemed an odd sort of woman.'

'I thought this job was nothing but trouble,' Mrs Jenkins said frankly. 'Until I'd left it, when I suddenly saw the troubles were nothing compared to the fun.'

'The same goes for life. As Mr Flintiron is sadly discovering.'

She raised her eyebrows. 'Did he have his op at the General?'

I sighed. 'Cancer of the colon. I thought it was diverticulitis, they could cut it out and he could live for years back in Australia. Bill Igtham did the surgery, and thought it could be diverticulitis, too. But the pathology report was definite, a fast-growing tumour. I'd have liked a chat with Dr Windrush about it, but he's gone on holiday in Italy. Poor old Flintiron! One of the best. He went into St Ethelnoth's Hospice last Monday.'

Mrs Jenkins looked gloomy. 'That's not the best address in Churchford. Mr Wynn phoned before you arrived this morning. He wants you to call. Didn't he go to Dr Quaggy?'

I asked sharply, 'Who said so?'

'Dr Quaggy. I met him in the Dingley Dell Coffee Shop.'

I ground my teeth. I said, 'Mr Whynn has forgiven everyone snared in that unhappy tangle, including Annabel.'

'She was a silly girl. The Attorney-General shouldn't have sent her to jail. He should have spanked her bottom.'

I arrived at the oast house after evening surgery. The foreign girl showed me into the circular sitting room, where Jim was opening a bottle of Highland Park.

'I got this stuff in specially for you. What do you know about St Ethelnoth's Hospice?' he asked cheerfully.

'A distinguished local institution from whose bourn no traveller returns.'

'And Mrs Huntington-Hartley, who runs it?'

'She has taken the sting out of death.'

'Nice?'

'A middle-aged blonde, fearsome in hip and tit. The sort who makes jam for charity, runs raffles for the church roof and is seen handing round cups of tea at scenes of disaster.'

'Oh, one of our national assets,' Jim observed. 'She wants me to be their new patron. The last chap completed the job by dying in the place.'

I sipped my malt. 'Seems a sound move. It enjoys a far better local reputation than the General Hospital, which tries to keep people out of it.'

He looked doubtful. 'These places give me the creeps. Going round shaking hands with a lot of living people is bad enough, dying ones would tax any politician's charm. Still, I suppose they wouldn't be full of difficult questions about their future. Could you find out more about the place for me?'

'As it happens, I've just got a patient there.'

'Splendid,' he said enthusiastically. 'Of course, St Ethelnoth's isn't part of the Health Service – it's a fund-raising job, really – but I must choose my company carefully in my present delicate state of political life.'

I promised him an appraisal of this ever-busy departure lounge.

'To rewind the panorama of life,' Jim continued, sticking

77

out his long legs in his armchair, 'how are you on this new idea of surrogate motherhood?'

'New? My dear fellow, a lot of funny things were happening on the surrogate scene in the Old Testament. What about Abram and his barren wife Sarai and Hagar the Egyptian *au pair*? A satisfactory arrangement all round, particularly as Abram was eighty-six at the time.'

Jim nodded, smiling. 'There's a debate before the recess. Parliament loves debating sex in any form, of course – embryos, rape, queers, dirty bookshops. It makes a refreshing change from the coal mines and the Official Secrets Act. I intend to speak. Showing a compassionate concern for the sexual problems of others might be helpful. Can you brief me on it?'

He poured me another Highland Park. 'Naturally, I don't expect you to do my dirty work for nothing, Richard, though it's a principle on which many politicians operate. You'll remember, before that girl behaved quite as unpleasantly towards me as Charlotte Corday to Marat in his bath – '

'With remission, she'll be released in a couple of months,' I interrupted.

'Really? Well, I expect she's getting quite used to the life. You were then briefing me on the National Health Service. All rather wasted, obviously I had to grab my chance with Resources, it's always happening in politics, as soon as a Cabinet minister begins to find his job comprehensible he's reshuffled. I mentioned a seat on the committee to advise HMG – Her Majesty's Government – about general practice.'

I nodded.

'I can still fix it. Forditch who runs Health is itching to collect a life peerage and make a pile in the City. He keeps in with me because he hopes the bank my father runs will assist in the bulldozing. Are you still keen?'

I pronounced, 'It would give me a feeling of attainment at the end of my career, which I am frightened to see closing without achieving all that I glimpsed in the vision of youth.

Was that pompous?' I asked anxiously.

Jim said amiably, 'No, you sound as though you were suffering from *Torschlusspanik*. That Scotch all right?'

'Just down the wrong way.'

'I believe you know our professional feminist, Ms Hortense Tankerton?'

'Bosom friend of Sandra's, if the sexist expression is allowed.'

'I don't think she's recovered from being overlooked for the Warnock Committee on surrogacy and embryos and such exciting things. I run into her at press parties. I gather she's staying with you tomorrow?'

I jumped up. 'She's bloody not!'

Jim shrugged. 'You'd better ask Sandra. Ms Tankerton seemed pretty sure of it. But she's so sure of everything.' He rose to see me out. 'How's the new Sir Basil?'

'Grateful they finally decided not to operate, and acting as if his family had been titled since the Norman Conquest. His wife's so overcome, she never leaves the house. A peculiar couple.'

Arriving home, I demanded fiercely, 'What's all this about Ms Hortense Tankerton?'

Sandra looked up from scraping the new potatoes.

'Yes, Hortense is staying a couple of nights,' she said calmly. 'Surely I mentioned it?'

'She's only just bloody left.'

'Nonsense! She hasn't visited us for two years.'

I reflected gloomily, 'Prometheus probably had the same feeling about the visits of the eagles.'

Sandra frowned. 'I don't get it.'

'He was chained to a rock, and the eagles arrived daily to breakfast on his liver. It continued over the ages.'

'Don't be insulting.'

'I'm not. I'm being classical.'

Sandra looked thoughtful. 'Thank you for reminding me, Hortense is allergic to breakfast cereals. She's lecturing the girls at St Ursula's. The headmistress says there's an epidemic of mumps, she's had to turn the visitors' room into an emergency sicker.'

'I know,' I shouted, 'I'm bloody MO at St Ursula's.'

'Your language really is becoming as bad as a soccer hooligan's. I wonder why you're so irritable these days?' she speculated murmuringly. 'Surely you've been through the male menopause? Anyway, Hortense is delightfully stimulating company. It was only jealousy about the utterly brilliant things she does for the Sunday papers and the BBC that kept her off the famous Warnock Committee. How did you hear she was coming?' she asked frankly.

I grew more tranquil, like Prometheus when the eagle had flown elsewhere for lunch.

'Jim Whynn seemed to know. He was asking again about that seat on the Government committee for GPs. I thought it would add a little warmth to the sunset of my career.'

'I wouldn't touch it.'

'Why?'

'Weren't you in the soup to your armpits with politicians already?'

'I can handle Jim Whynn or any other human,' I boasted. 'Doctors, priests, magistrates and officers know men as thoroughly as if they had made them. Sartre said so.'

She shook her head. 'You're far too honest, dear.'

I thought of Mrs Osgood. Conscience tore, like the eagle coming for second helps.

I left home next morning in a bad temper. I was short with Mrs Jenkins. She announced she would not submit to verbal mugging, and was perfectly capable of resigning all over again, in mid-surgery if necessary.

She swept out, sweeping in Mr and Mrs Cluff.

They were a decent, thirtyish couple. He was an insurance agent, she a salesperson at Robbins Modes, Churchford's fashionable *couturier*. For ten years they had been earnestly trying to have a baby, I got the impression every night.

'You sent us to Mr Taverill at the General, who said it was my fault,' Mrs Cluff remarked with misplaced guilt.

80

'So that AID business wouldn't work with us,' Mr Cluff reminded me glumly.

'What's the frozen embryo thing?' she asked hesitantly.

I was in no mood for fertility lectures. I explained shortly, 'The wife's eggs are removed through her tummy with an instrument resembling an apple-picker, then mixed with the husband's sperm in a test-tube to produce an embryo, which can be frozen in liquid nitrogen and placed in her womb at the *moment critique*. It's difficult to do and the doctors are difficult to find, also it's getting up the nose of high-minded persons.'

'Sounds a bit scary,' she said uneasily.

They looked at each other.

'Doctor, could you contact one of those surrogate motherhood agencies for us?' suggested Mr Cluff.

I slapped the consulting desk. 'Certainly not! They're utterly unethical. If not criminal. They are outlawed by Parliament. They absolutely stink in the nostrils of high-minded persons. Surely you saw it on the telly?'

She sighed. 'We do so want a child.'

'So do all normal humans,' I told her briskly. 'But many high-minded ones have forgotten the urge because they're comfortably furnished with sufficient of their own.' I conceded, 'Surrogation for money may bring more alarming complications than Little Buttercup's baby farming in *HMS Pinafore*, but there's nothing against an amateur arrangement with your sisters, and your cousins, and your still fertile aunts.'

They left undecided and unhappy. I felt shamefully I had been crustily unsympathetic. I consoled myself that the most harmful effect of fashionable genetic mucking-about was widespread overexcitement.

That afternoon I was sitting in Mrs Huntington-Hartley's bright, flower-decked office in St Ethelnoth's Hospice, three converted and combined roomy Victorian villas at the same end of Churchford as my own.

'We look death squarely in the face,' she was informing me.

81

I nodded solemnly.

'There's a sad thing about death, Dr Gordon. It is never discussed freely and uninhibitedly in everyday life. It is the last taboo in an age which has become perfectly conceited about its defiance of conventions. All of us here talk about death as permissively as those outside talk about sex.'

'Both happens between the sheets,' I observed, but she gave me a sideways look.

'At St Ethelnoth's we are creative about death,' she continued chillingly. 'For instance, we give all painkillers by mouth in exactly the same quantity of fluid, so the patients don't know when we're pepping up the dose.'

I nodded admiringly.

'My life's ambition is that everyone should die happy.'

I nodded politely.

Unlike my own patients, hers could never complain afterwards about the treatment.

'Your Mr Flintiron –' she began.

'A sad case.'

She tightened her lips.

'He is being rather difficult. But of course he is an Australian,' she conceded charitably.

Jeff Flintiron was a middle-aged bachelor who had ventured back to the Old Country and like Mr Rupert Murdoch and Mr Barry Humphries made a fortune from it. He was in pet food. Though Jeff was as coy about the contents of his tins as Sweeny Todd about those of his pies, they had an appeal as powerful and mysterious as Homer's lotus.

The longer Jeff stayed in England the more he became Australian. The kangaroo was his sacred cow. The boomerang his Excalibur. Botany wool his Golden Fleece. A tube of Foster's his Holy Grail. There were similarly no more British British than the British in India. Jeff was the Raj in reverse.

I enquired sombrely of Mrs Huntington-Hartley how he was settling in.

She consulted a chart.

'Mood 9,' she said disapprovingly. 'That's bottom of the

scale. We award them marks once a week on the gloom index. They also get a rage rating. Dying makes some people extremely angry. I regret that he is rather destroying the happy family atmosphere I strive for here. You'll find him in Daisy Ward.'

She rose from her desk.

'I do hope that Mr Whynn will soon be an active force in politics again,' she said feelingly. 'He will be invaluable in raising money for us, as we must, like the old voluntary hospitals with their everlasting collecting-boxes before Nye Bevan nationalized them. I felt the least I could do in return was awarding our cooking and cleaning contracts to the firm which – you may know – his wife has an interest in.'

I did not know. I wondered who else in Churchford did.

She directed me past Lavender, Forget-me-not, Cowslip and Candytuft to a sunny, three-bedded ward in which Jeff was sitting against the pillows wearing a sunflower-patterned silk dressing gown and clutching a bunch of pink gladioli. He was a skinny, sparse-haired, leather-faced man, who responded gloomily to my hearty enquiry about how he felt, 'Like a baboon with a sunkissed arse.'

Australians have as impressive an ability to hit about the language as the cricket ball.

'These places would give Superman the creeping goose-pimples. Ta, love,' he addressed a young nurse handing him a medicine-glass of white fluid. 'I'd prefer a cold tinnie.'

She smiled tolerantly. 'You always say that, Mr Flint-iron.'

He gulped, grimacing. 'Know what, doc? They give painkillers here always in the same volume of fluid. So's you don't rumble the dose is going up. See? You gotta go along with it. It takes two to tango, even round a deathbed. They try hard to cheer us up, so we cheer up to cheer them up, gettit?'

I murmured, 'You can't blame them for trying to keep your mind of . . . er, things.'

He said dejectedly, 'I bet even the band on the *Titanic*

playing *Yes, We Have No Bananas* couldn't keep the customers' minds off the ice-cold water shortly reaching up to their expectations.'

I asked how he found the staff.

'The chaplain seems a decent bloke, but perhaps only because he knows I'm going to meet his boss before he does. We sing a hymn every morning. Well, I suppose it's never too late to enjoy new experiences, and there's not much else to do except watch breakfast TV. They keep telling me I've reached the time when I'm facing reality. Personally, I think it's just the time when I don't want to. This is Mrs Watkins.'

I had been eyeing curiously the pink and pleasant lady in a lemon-yellow linen dress with a book on her lap sitting at the bedside.

'Mrs Watkins brought me the gladdies to make me feel at home. Her husband croaked here.'

'Dr Gordon, isn't it?' She smilingly offered her hand. 'I come every afternoon to read Mr Flintiron P.G. Wodehouse.'

Jeff grumbled, 'I prefer a good murder with lots of bodies.'

'We've got to the screamingly funny bit about Gussie Fink-Nottle presenting the prizes, haven't we?' she reminded him, opening the book and running her finger eagerly down the page.

'Don't let me keep you from your fun,' I said hastily.

I slipped away. Those damned from here to Eternity make harrowing company – particularly when they have hardly any distance to go.

At the front door I met Dr Quaggy.

'What a wonderful woman, Mrs Huntington-Hartley,' he greeted me in his voice like well-oiled machinery.

He was tall, handsome and silver-haired, with a moustache like iron filings under a magnet.

'So magnificent, how she makes the inescapable less intolerable,' he added admiringly. 'And how are *you*, Richard?'

'Splendid!' I said sharply. The surroundings provoked a defiant answer.

'That appalling mess with Jim Whynn must have been a terrible strain,' he continued sympathetically. 'Do you know what *I* should have done?'

'No?'

'Instantly retired and gone to live in the Algarve.'

'I have as little desire to live in the Algarve as in Alaska.'

He chuckled. 'But Sandra has. Everyone in Churchford knows that.'

'Everyone except me.'

'May I tell you something in confidence, and with frankness, Richard?'

His grey eyes held mine in a solicitous embrace.

'We are such old friends,' he assured me, 'it is something best not to stay hidden. After you'd exposed all Jim Whynn's faults and feebleness in the newspapers, he decided to transfer his family from your practice to mine. Understandable, Richard, I'm sure you'll admit? You're a fair man. I want you to know that I refused to take them. Firmly and repeatedly – he asked several times. I advised him that, for all the disgrace he had suffered, it was inadvisable for any man to change his doctor until he made a mess of his treatment.'

I thanked him.

12

I finished evening surgery. Ms Tankerton would be at home.
I should have preferred entertaining Dracula suffering from
anaemia. I recalled she would shortly be leaving to lecture. I
could agreeably avoid meeting her by stopping at the Blue
Boar.

It was hot, the surgery empty. While drawing my pint of
Old Kentish Double Hop (the only ale), our popular, come-
ly, thirty-fiveish barmaid Belinda offered as conversation,
'What about surrogate motherhood, then?'

I folded my arms thoughtfully on the bar.

'Do you realize that until recently the only surrogate
things were bishops?'

'Strikes me as just another craze, like aerobics and the
F-plan diet.'

I said emphatically, 'I think you're right. Because everyone starts talking about something doesn't increase its importance.'

'But there's money in it?' she suggested.

I told her, 'The going rate appears to be £6500, though
God knows how they calculate it.'

'Divide that by nine months, then by four . . .' she worked
out. 'Mm, 180 quid a week. You'd never touch that as a
dinner-lady.'

She handed me my change, adding contemplatively, 'I
wouldn't say no, just for a bit of how's-your-father with some
feller, even if he looked like Kojak in a toupee.'

I agreed, 'Fanny Hill in her prime couldn't command that
sort of money. But unfortunately that's not the way the
performance of the obstetrical trio is conducted.'

She looked blank. 'Go on?'

'We use a syringe,' I explained.

She gave a sexy glance. 'You'd do it? Well, I wouldn't mind.'

I told her hastily, 'No, there are doctors specializing in it, same as heart transplants. Though I believe there's a D-I-Y kit, to cut down the expense. I expect you can buy it at Boot's. Or maybe Halford's.'

'You like cheese-and-onion flavour, don't you?'

'Please.'

Her green eyes took on a speculative gaze. 'You mean, the bloke puts his whatnot in a syringe and comes round with it in his sponge-bag, or whatever?'

I nodded. 'That's the general idea.'

She wrinkled her nose. 'Bit finicky, isn't it? I mean, like peeling grapes. What's wrong with direct action?'

I snapped a crisp. 'There seems an emotional difference about love being delivered by the syringeful.'

'Wouldn't I end up with quins, or a whole football team?' she enquired, wiping an ashtray.

'No, that's something different. The famous test-tube. They implant in the mother's womb several eggs at once.'

'Why?'

'To ensure successful sprouting. Same principle as sowing marrows.'

She arranged the coasters with a pensive pout. 'You know my husband Brian?'

I nodded. He was a slight, cheerful man with a bushy moustache, a comic T-shirt and comic tattoos. Belinda had prodded him into an assortment of jobs, but he found unemployment more restful. He was a contented layabout, a man to be envied.

'And our Kevin?' she added.

I nodded again. A bright, bookish fourteen-year-old.

Belinda's face brightened. 'Kevin's doing wonderfully at the Beowulf Comprehensive. I had to go and see the head teacher. They want him to go to university. Shall I fill you up?'

'No, I must be getting along.'

87

'But it needs money.'

'You get a grant,' I pointed out.

'So the head teacher told me. But he'd need a bit more. Being skint while you're being educated is like it raining all your holiday, if you ask me. And I'm not making a fortune pulling pints, you know that.'

She swept my crumpled crisp packet from the bar. 'I wouldn't mind doing a bit of surrogating to pay for it. Could you find me anything, doctor?'

This fascinating proposition was halted by the arrival of a pair of regulars demanding their usual.

'You've just missed Hortense,' Sandra said as I arrived home.

'What a pity,' I said.

I sat down with a quiet Glenfiddich, reflecting how pleasant any of life's activities were if performed without the company of Ms Hortense Tankerton.

I reached idly for *Right Ho, Jeeves* and turned to the arrival of teetotal Gussie Fink-Nottle at Market Snodsbury Grammar School, stewed to the eyebrows on orange juice thoughtfully spiked by Bertie Wooster with gin.

My mind strayed from the sunshine of P.G. Wodehouse into the shadows of Jeff Flintiron. He had been my patient for ten years. He had no family, nor seemingly friends. I should be a good sort if I called every day to cheer him up. I should have done the same, had Prometheus been a patient.

'And how are you feeling this morning?' I enquired cheerily on my way home from surgery next day.

'Like a stuffed dingo with moth,' he replied morosely.

As I commiserated, he enlarged, 'Not that I'm in pain. Come to think of it, I've been pretty perky in myself since moving in. I reckon the rest is doing me good. But they keep your nose to the tombstone, no mistake. They go on about wanting me to die with dignity. Me, Jeff Flintiron, who's never done anything dignified in his life. If I'd got married, I'd have done it in thongs, with a carnation stuck up my Bondi sweatshirt. So when I croak I'm going to feel bloody awkward being on my dignity, aren't I? I'll be like the Queen waving to the onlookers while someone pulls the rug from under her Guccis.'

I put it tactfully that when the time came he must feel free to behave exactly as he liked.

'And another thing, doc.'

Jeff crossed his hands on his chest.

'I do not wish to end up in the local cremmie,' he said firmly. 'I do not! I've been there with various acquaintances, the turnover is colossal, it's a McDonald's in human-burgers.'

He mused, 'It's the one service you *don't* want quick. I'd like people having enough time to brood that I wasn't such a bad old sod after all, not that there'd be much of a house, I can't expect standing room only with all my relatives down under, can I? That's why I wish the husk returned to where it came from. Woollabillabong, just outside Sydney. Can you fix it?'

I readily agreed to execute his last request.

'You'd better hurry,' he added glumly. 'Mrs Watkins has started reading me the short stories.'

Early that evening I called at Templar Funeral Services (Personal Supervision) in Churchford High Street.

As a GP has on average ten patients a year dying in their own homes, I had become well acquainted with Mr Aitcheson the boss undertaker, who always welcomed me with an air of eager, deferential assistance. I suppose a high-class fence was the same on receiving Raffles.

He was a tall, lean, youngish bright-eyed man with side-whiskers as solidly decorative as coffin handles, sitting amid highly-polished mahogany and leather and cut-glass bowls of white roses in his consulting room. He led me to a small office decorated with photographs depicting Great Funerals of Yesteryear, when important customers were hauled to their eternal rest by sufficient black horses to shift the artillery to Mafeking.

'No problem,' he returned airily as I relayed Jeff's needs.

'Everybody's doing it. Cup of tea, doctor? Or would you prefer something stronger? Oh, yes, about a couple of thousand become deceased on holiday every year,' he enlightened me. 'It's what you'd expect, doctor, eh? I mean, all that sudden snorkelling and skiing, not to mention the pernod and ouzo.'

He grinned. 'Why, the cargo sheds at Heathrow can get like a horizontal package tour in August. Thanks, love,' he addressed the pretty blonde girl in a black dress appearing with the tea and a Swiss roll.

I enquired about the itch to get home.

'As you'd expect, doctor, it goes against the deceased's family's sense of what is right and decent, leaving them there on the Costa del whatever. I mean, a holiday's something you go on to enjoy yourself. But we manage to cope. There's a lot of exciting things happening in undertaking these days,' he informed me. 'Funny, but it's the Poles who've got the edge on all of us in deceased transport. Ever heard of BONGO?'

I frowned. 'A show in the West End?'

'Stands in Polish for the Bureau of Preservation of Foreign Graves,' he rolled off. 'It's run by their government. I expect you know, a lot of Poles over the years have for one reason or another gone elsewhere. When they become deceased, they leave instructions for transportation back to the old country. Wonderfully patriotic, the Poles. Mind, I don't suppose these days they'd go back home if they had to live there, so it's the most comfortable way of expressing their feelings. BONGO airlifts five hundred of them a year over the Iron Curtain, they make a killing in dollars.'

I expressed wonderment at the easy-going application of capitalist principles to ex-ex-Poles.

'Mind you, bringing them home to rest isn't cheap in anyone's currency,' he asserted. 'The form-filling alone is a week's work. Every country's different. I mean, Spain, now. I ask you, it's complicated enough just to have a motor accident there, isn't it? Then there's the export licence.'

I reflected that if I contented Dr Quaggy and retired to the Algarve, I should finally come home as the bureaucratic equivalent of a hogshead of port.

'It all takes time,' he explained wearily. 'The deceased has to go on board an hour before the other passengers. After all, a lot of people are nervous about flying anyway. You've got to embalm them, otherwise, well, the baggage handlers would put the boot in for dirty money, wouldn't they?'

I suggested that Mr Aitcheson visit Jeff at St Ethelnoth's to discuss management of the impending situation. He promised to call the following afternoon, between cases. I left reflecting solemnly on the remark of C.P. Snow's – 'This body is not, cannot be, all I am – that is the human cry.'

Unfortunately – I bleakly think like most doctors – it is.

Perhaps we are too attached to our work.

13

Mrs Huntington-Hartley intercepted me in the lupin-festooned hallway of St Ethelnoth's the following sunny evening.

'Dr Gordon,' she greeted me sharply. 'I should be obliged if you would not arrange to have undertakers arriving at the front door.'

I wondered nervously if he should have used the trades-man's entrance.

'They do not fit into our conception of death.'

I apologized, though mentioning it could be no more upsetting than meeting the surgeon who was going to per-form some dreadful operation on you.

'Further,' she informed me huffily, 'Mr Flintiron is being a handful. He does not seem to fit into, or even appreciate, the spirit of the Hospice at all.'

I asked guiltily what he was up to.

'You'd better see for yourself.' She started to close her office door. 'As for Mrs Watkins, I can only say I'm sur-prised.'

Jeff was sitting on the edge of his bed donning a pair of houndstooth trousers. Mrs Watkins stood beside him clutch-ing *Blandings Castle*, purse-lipped and pinker.

I asked cheerily how he was.

'Like a barbecued cockatoo on a wowsers' outing,' he replied disgruntledly.

'Do you know how much that stiffs' chauffeur wanted,' he demanded indignantly, 'just to plant me back among my roots? Twice the bloody first-class air fare! And not even free champagne. So I said, Look, matey, why not stick the remains in a wheelchair, wrap them in a warm tartan rug, provide them with a flight bag and some maggies, and pass them off as a disabled going to enjoy returning health and strength from the sea air at Bondi? But this carcass courier just rabbited on about the cost of regulation hermetically-sealed, zinc-lined coffins, which don't come secondhand, accommodation at overnight stopovers and the lost baggage insurance. So I've cancelled the ticket by Vampire Airlines. Pass us that pink shirt, love,' he instructed Mrs Watkins, stripping off his pyjama jacket.

'I'd rather leave the cash to Mrs Watkins here,' he decided. 'Who says I'm beginning to remind her of her husband.'

'I don't know if Mrs Huntington-Hartley would entirely approve,' she said anxiously.

'Why should she get on your back?' he insisted crossly. 'Enjoy life! Why don't we both fly to Australia economy class, and I can die there instead? It would work out cheaper than me alone in a plank seat.'

She exclaimed, 'I've always wanted to see men with corks dangling from their hats. And of course the Opera House. Though Mrs Huntington-Hartley would think it all most irregular.'

'Why?' Jeff tugged up his zip.

'Nobody's ever left here before,' she explained. 'Alive, I mean.'

'C'mon, Sheila, we're going walkabout,' he decided, knotting his tie. 'I feel a real box of birds this afto. If I wasn't in this place, I wouldn't think I was going to die for one moment. We'll phone Quantas. Maybe find a cold tinnie, eh?'

'Oh, Jeff!' She clasped her hands. 'You are such a lively soul!'

I had to leave. Sandra had warned me that were I not prompt to dine with Ms Tankerton she would leave me and I should have to iron my own shirts.

'I want to talk to you seriously about the womb,' Ms Tankerton was inviting an hour later over our dinner table.

'Fine,' I told her.

'That mysterious organ!' she continued enthusiastically. 'Shaped like the very avocados we are eating. Do you know, it positively *frightens* doctors, theologians, lawyers, politicians, even the most complacent of great statesmen. Why?'

'You tell me,' I suggested.

Leaning close across the table, she revealed, 'Because it is the *very essence of femaleness.*'

Ms Tankerton was fat with round glasses, as feminine as a Japanese Sumo wrestler.

'A very beautiful thought,' agreed Sandra.

'I always looked on it as a gynaecologists' gold mine,' I said.

'Typical male chauvinist medicine,' Ms Tankerton responded contemptuously, splashing her *vinaigrette*.

Sandra's look revealed that she knew my slipping into the kitchen a couple of times before dinner was for extra Glenfiddich from the bottle prudently cached in the plate cupboard. She had warned me not to behave like with her brother George at Christmas.

'Men no better understand the womb than birth positions, lesbian motherhood, Women Against the Bomb and wholefood cookery.'

'I expect not,' I agreed.

'Artificial insemination!' she exclaimed. 'Thanks, I will have another drop of that Chablis. How sickeningly unaesthetic to fructify the womb like squeezing toothpaste. The moment of conception was intended to be one of ecstasy.'

'A widely held view,' I concurred.

'The divine feminine function of the womb is to nurture the juice of human passion,' she asserted, vigorously scraping her avocado skin. 'Surrogate motherhood! Hawking one's womb on the open market. An outrage in the face of femininity. Oh, steak-and-kidney pudding, Sandra, how lovely.'

I wondered when I might take the night air, in the direction of the Blue Boar.

'Womb shall call to womb!' Ms Tankerton declared. 'The

sistership of the womb is worldwide, more embracing than the Roman Catholic Church and communism combined. Were it sensibly organized, it would be an overpowering force in the destiny of the world. Just imagine, Richard! A world run by women instead of abominably dominated by men. No more wars, no terrorists, no muggers, everyone united in caring love,' she outlined, eyes radiant. 'Sandra this is utterly delicious, though I daren't think what it's doing to my weight.'

I wondered if she was insane. But people are never so stupid as when they are trying to be clever.

'What's your opinion on gays, Richard?'

'A lot of them aren't, of course,' I replied mildly. 'They're just trying to attract attention, like naughty children. The rest are only the emotionally immature. The biological urge may be all-powerful, but it takes a certain amount of sophistication to take your trousers down in front of a strange woman.'

She looked shocked. 'The medical profession is still living in *Tom Brown's Schooldays*.'

'Oh, we have a Gay Medical Association, you know,' I informed her. 'Very erudite on AIDS. I fancy I had one of their members as a locum last summer. He took as extraordinary pains to hide it as I not to notice it. Wasted a lot of valuable practice time.'

'Another glass? Thanks. Womb power, Richard! It could be a force more terrifying than The Bomb.'

Sandra sighed. 'Never do I hear conversation at home like this.'

It struck me that Belinda in the Blue Boar was better balanced on the womb than Ms Tankerton, probably than the entire Warnock Committee. If anyone wanted to lease a womb, why not? It was only pre-emptive adoption.

As Sandra continued to bathe in the Jacuzzi of Ms Tankerton's opinions, I wondered dare I act the honest baby-broker between Belinda and the Cluffs? With young Kevin so bright and her husband Brian as dim as a road lamp,

95

Belinda's genes were a readily marketable commodity. Should I be committing my second offence in three months? Money need not change hands – well, no more ostentatiously than the tenners which amateur rugby players happen to find in their boots.

After breakfast the following morning I enthusiastically waved goodbye to Ms Tankerton.

'No golf?' asked Sandra. 'It's Saturday.'

'I've got to write up this surrogate motherhood stuff for Jim Whynn.'

'Hortense would have been an enormous help,' she chided me. 'We should have got her to stay for the weekend.'

I had a folder of cuttings from newspapers, the *BMJ* and the *Lancet*, supplied by my young friend Dr Lonelyhearts. He made more money in more comfort than most doctors by running his practice on paper. As Our Medical Correspondent, his glittering sentences shone clinical erudition through the thoughtful papers. As A Doctor Speaks in the women's magazines, he wrote with the suave authority of a sophisticated lover choosing the wine, on such irksome human predicaments as, *Are Others Conscious of My Smelly Feet?* and *Is It Unhealthy That My Husband Is Insatiable?* and *Can You Get Pregnant From Using the Same Bath as Men?* Every bookshop displayed his cheerful paperbacks giving advice on sex and on diet – which he confessed from the widespread failure of their results might be interchangeable.

I worked hard, thinking of others on England's fairways green. I finished as the grandfather clock was chiming two on Monday morning and went to bed. At six the telephone rang beside me. It was Jack Windrush.

'Richard! I'm just back from holiday.'

He sounded frantic.

'Have a good time?' I mumbled sleepily.

'A catastrophe has struck.'

'Oh? Burgled?' I suggested. 'Lost luggage? Daphne gone off with an Italian waiter?'

I felt he could have been less impatient, sharing everyday travellers' tales of doom.

'My locum. At the General. Doing my pathology work while I was away. You've heard?'

'Heard what?'

I blinked dozily. Sandra snuggled beside me.

'Last night. He's been whipped into the bin under an escort of five psychiatrists. Schizophrenia, mania, paranoia, dementia, you name it. When I gave him the job, he seemed a perfectly ordinary Irishman. Makes you think, doesn't it?' he reflected. 'Makes you wonder how many of our fellow-doctors are getting away with it as raving madmen.'

I consoled him, 'It's a good job you're back before harm's done.'

'Harm done? God! I've been up all night reading his reports. They've been going to all our physicians and surgeons over the past month. Every bloody thing wrong. All his microscope findings cockeyed. The man's wrecked the entire work of the General. Your Mr Flintiron, for instance –'

'What's the matter?' cried Sandra, as I jumped from my pillow.

I asked breathlessly, 'He's all right?'

'As rain. No cancer at all. The slide under the microscope looks plumb normal. All set for a long life, which he will pass in comfort from the damages extracted from us. Can you get hold of him?'

'Easily. He's gone to St Ethelnoth's to die.'

'Well, they tell me it's very comfortable,' said Jack, ringing off.

I jumped out of bed and pulled on my clothes, as frantically as the morning of Jim Whynn's revelations. I hurried round to St Ethelnoth's. I hoped that the bird had flown to Australia. It could all be awkward with Mrs Huntington-Hartley.

Jeff was sitting up in bed eating boiled eggs while Mrs Watkins read him *The Code of the Woosters*.

I broke the glad news.

Silence.

Then Mrs Watkins howled, went pinker and threw P.G. Wodehouse in the air.

Jeff said calmly, 'Funny thing, doc, I felt all along I wasn't going to snuff. But it seemed only polite to feel worse every day, just to cheer up the staff. I mean, they're lovely people, you gotta assure them they're doing a worthwhile job, haven't you?'

'Jeffrey!' Mrs Watkins clasped him.

'Watch out, darling! You'll squeeze the life out of me. Doc, I want you to meet the wife. Still to be, of course.'

I congratulated the doubly happy couple.

'We fixed a couple of tickets with Quantas – one single, one return,' he explained. 'Might as well use them, eh, love? After all,' he expanded to me, 'when a bloke's been preparing himself for Heaven twenty-four-hours a day for a week, he's ready to settle for the next best thing. Which is among the gladdies and the possums and the gum trees, as any dinkum Aussie can tell you. C'mon, Sheila!'

He swung out of bed.

'Let's escape from God's waiting room,' he said determinedly. 'Nothing makes a man enjoy life better than getting a slice of it back on a plate. It's like a nice steak after being stuck in a cell and starved. Who's going to tell Mrs Huntington-Hartley?'

'The doctor,' said Mrs Watkins.

Mrs Huntington-Hartley accepted the premature departure of her guest graciously.

'But how are *you*, doctor?' she enquired.

'Fine! It's a lovely morning.'

She gave me a steely look. 'You appear distinctly peaky to me. Are you *sure* you're absolutely well?'

Fear gripped me. Mrs Huntington-Hartley had the eye of a highly experienced Valkyrie.

'Of course, it may be absolutely nothing,' she continued with brisk solicitude. 'But if it isn't, Dr Gordon, please *do* remember that you will always be sure of a very warm welcome in here. Good morning.'

I left reflecting that Mrs Huntington-Hartley and all the devoted people in hospices do wonderful and selfless work, sparing distraught families by clearing up the emotional and sometimes physical mess. Though I should prefer not to become stuck in the one-way system to the Pearly Gates in an organized coach party. When the time comes, I shall buy a case of Glenfiddich and lock myself in the loo.

I saw the Cluffs a fortnight later. They had done it naturally.

I congratulated them.

'The very thought,' announced Mrs Cluff vibrantly, 'of my husband impregnating an unknown woman was quite enough to stimulate the whatever it is.'

I agreed. Human fertility is a mechanism as delicate as a Fabergé clock. God knows what influences it. Possibly the moon earns its place in love songs.

After that evening surgery I stopped at the Blue Boar. It was pouring, and the snuggery was empty. I was relieved that my ethical problem had vapourized. It would have anyway been as difficult to manage tactfully as a house-agent getting two couples to share a holiday villa on the Costa del Sol.

Belinda greeted me, 'Remember I was rabbiting on about that surrogate motherhood? You like it in a mug, don't you?'

'Please.'

'Well, I've done something better. I've read the riot act to my Brian. He can get a job pretty easily. Everyone likes him. The brewers have taken him on as a loader, and this time he promises solemnly he'll stick to it. Mind, it's not a fortune, but with my little bit it'll all help our young Kevin to get on in the world. Maybe become a doctor?'

I expressed good wishes towards this end.

'He's already got a lot of the doctor in him – keeps telling people to do what's best for them.'

99

'I must congratulate both parents on having such a clever son.'

'There's no cheese-and-onion tonight. Prawn cocktail flavour do you?'

'Thanks.'

She handed the packet across the bar with a Gioconda smile.

'Between you and me, doctor, fifteen years ago I was surrogated.'

This fascinating conversation was halted by the arrival of a bunch of regulars demanding their usual.

14

I drove from Foxglove Lane to Chaucer Way the following fine morning, meditating how humanity, like its activities, had become irksomely complicated since 1662.

The Prayer Book then had simple categories. The quick and the dead. These have been bothersomely extended to the unborn and the dying, who had flexed my moral muscles the previous month. The handicapped, the disabled, the deprived, the geriatric, the transplanted, the comatose formed equally distinct groups demanding sympathy and ethics. Arriving at the surgery I discovered another. The survivors.

'Mrs Rosie Styles of Inkerman Villas,' Mrs Jenkins greeted me. 'The community nurse wants you to call. The lady's getting on a bit.'

I drove after my morning's patients to a gently undulating street of terraced Victorian two-up-two-downs across the railway line.

Mrs Rosie Styles was white, wrinkled and wizened, with knobbly arthritic hands. She sat in a red plush armchair, wearing a dingy print dress and clasping a stout stick, amid heavy well-polished furniture, a mantelpiece with a tasselled red cover, framed samplers and an aspidistra.

I examined her fingers and said – the jolly doctor – 'You must be nearing ninety?'

She stared, outraged.

'ON SATURDAY WEEK,' she screeched, 'I AM ONE HUNDRED!'

'You don't look it,' I added hastily. 'Not a bit. Well, you'll have a telegram from the Queen, won't you, which will be nice. She must be already thinking about it.'

'IT'S THE DANDELIONS,' she shouted, having like many wearers of the NHS hearing aid the impression that everyone else in the world lacked one.

I said, 'Is it?'

She nodded vigorously. 'DANDELIONS.'

An allergy? I glanced round the neat room. Nothing but a bowl of dried heathers and a vase of pampas grass.

She explained, 'EAT DANDELION LEAVES FOR LONG LIFE. MY FATHER TOLD ME THAT WHEN HE CAME HOME FROM THE TERRIBLE WAR.'

'Oh, I see,' I observed sagely, 'They must have been difficult to come by, dandelions, in the trenches of France.'

She stared with contempt. 'DID YOU SAY FRANCE? *FRANCE*? I JUST DON'T UNDERSTAND YOU YOUNG PEOPLE THESE DAYS. THE TERRIBLE WAR WAS IN SOUTH AFRICA, EVERYONE KNOWS THAT.'

I enquired the other secrets of longevity.

'STRICT VEGETARIAN DIET ESPECIALLY PRUNES, RENOUNCE THE DEMON DRINK AND THE STINKING WEED, LIVE A CHASTE LIFE AND BED AT TEN.'

I expressed admiration of these principles and warmly wished her many more years yet.

'I SHOULD HOPE SO.' She gave an unexpected grin of NHS teeth. 'I WANT TO KNOW HOW EVERYTHING TURNS OUT IN *CROSSROADS* JUST LIKE THE REST OF THE COUNTRY, DON'T I?'

The *rarae aves* of general practice come like magpies in pairs.

The next afternoon I was summoned by the health visitor to Mr Harold Wooljohn of Khartoum Crescent. I drove to a short street of tumbledown cement-faced villas beyond the gas works.

Mr Wooljohn was pale, podgy and ponky, with anaemia. He sat in an untidy two-room, ground-floor flat, wearing corduroy trousers and a bright tartan shirt.

I pulled down his lower eyelid to assess the pallor of its lining, saying cheerfuly, 'You must be nearing ninety?'

He interrupted lighting a roll-up to give me a cagey glance.

'You must be joking,' he suggested hoarsely.

'Sorry!' I added hastily. 'Taking another look, you're not a day over eighty.'

'Trying to borrow a quid, or something?' he asked derisively. 'I was selling papers barefoot at the King's coronation.'

'Really?' I enquired, interested. 'Which king?'

'He had a beard.' He wheezily blew out a cloud of smoke and added modestly, 'I'm a hundred on Friday week.'

'How remarkable! You certainly don't look it,' I told him forcefully. 'You'll enjoy the singular honour of a telegram from the Queen.'

'I'd rather enjoy one of them birds with fishnet stockings doing a kissogram,' he said.

'I'm sure that can be arranged, too. What do you put it down to, scoring this enviable century?'

He shrugged his bulky shoulders.

'Living naturally, I s'pose,' he decided. 'I always eat what grub I feel like. It's a crime you can't get them pigs' trotters like what I remember, not to mention the meat pies, they had gravy like treacle. Reckon I take a few pints a day. Gotta keep yer kidneys flushed, aintcher?'

'Indeed,' I concurred.

He inspected his crumpled, soggy-ended cigarette.

'Fags may kill you,' he reasoned, 'but they don't me, and that's all I'm worried about.'

Feeling it churlish to disagree, I asked, 'Are you married?'

He nodded. 'Yes. Often. But not as such.'

He choked for half a minute on the smoke. Wiping his bulbous eyes with his sleeve, he reflected, 'Reckon a regular goose-and-duck keeps a bloke young, as well as out of mischief. Waddya say, doctor?'

'It is the message of many modern sex manuals.'

'Mind, I had to give it up a few years back, when I couldn't get around so easily.'

103

I commiserated.

'Someone pinched my bike,' he explained disgruntedly.

I gave directions to visit the General and have a specimen of his blood examined.

'It was a real pity about the bike,' he reflected sombrely. 'I mean, any man wants to get a little bit more in before it's too late even to bother thinking about it.'

I nodded. 'That's called *Torschlusspanik!*'

'I thought it was,' he agreed.

I drove to the golf club meditating that – for all the miracles of modern medicine – we each have an inbuilt clock which for only a mystical few ticks away a century. It was an aphorism I had noticed in the *BMJ* by the Emeritus Regius Professor of Medicine at Oxford, who still has an agreeable number of years to keep chiming.

In the club bar was Arthur Crevin, a short, pink, fat, grey-haired, bristly-moustached man, a dreadful golfer and editor of the *Churchford Echo*. I mentioned my last two days' work producing an interesting double ton achieved by the local population.

He suddenly became excited, spilling his pink gin.

'Here I am, complaining that we've had no decent news in Churchford since the headmaster in the bus shelter. And you're casually pitching headlines right on the pin. *Two* of them becoming king-sized senior citizens the same weekend? Know what I'm going to do? Nice little party, champagne and *canapés* at the Churchford Arms Hotel. Oh, it'll make a lovely story! I'll be proud to present the healthiest town in the nation. Superb publicity. I can twist the Chamber of Commerce for thousands of quids' worth of advertising.'

I murmured that the pair might prefer to keep the day a secret between them and the Queen.

'Would *you*?' Arthur demanded, producing a notebook. 'You're only a hundred once, you know. Oh, they're freaks, but revered freaks. It's instant ancestor-worship.'

The *Echo* appeared two mornings later. Pictures of Rosie and Harold covered half the front page under the headline

WE'RE 200! In the story filling the rest of the page I was mentioned as the doctor to both. I felt this useful advertising.

I arrived with the paper proudly under my arm at morning surgery, to find Mrs Jenkins looking nervous.

'Two telephone calls already this morning, doctor,' she announced. 'From Mr Hosegood of Mons Avenue and Mrs Lambert of Himalaya Drive.'

I frowned. 'They're not patients of mine, are they? What's the matter with them?'

'No, they're not, doctor. They're both very angry. They're a hundred and one and not in the papers.'

'All four in Churchford? How remarkable,' I exclaimed cheerfully. 'I'll phone Arthur Crevin at once. He'll be doubly delighted.'

Arthur was not delighted at all.

'Not another lot of senile scroungers?' he groaned. 'I've had four on the line already this morning, and I haven't yet finished my breakfast. That's eight who should have been decently dead thirty years ago. The champagne's out. It's going to be wine and cheese upstairs at the Blue Boar.'

I arrived home that evening to discover a Porsche outside the front gate and inside the house young Dr Lonelyhearts enjoying a Glenlivet with Sandra.

Dr Lonelyhearts was Dr Aleyn Price-Browne BM of Oxford, married to Dr Josephine from Guy's. They lived not far from Foxglove Lane. He was tall, gingery and genial, dressed in slacks and yellow sports shirt.

'Is there life after geriatrics?' he greeted me cheerfully. 'Dr Gordon says "Yes!" I'll put it in my next piece for Fleet Street.'

'Oh, there's a centennial epidemic,' I informed him. I poured myself a malt, recounting my conversation with Arthur Crevin.

'There's a whole two thousand of them in the country. Didn't you know?' he imparted casually. 'We support ten times the centenarians of thirty years ago.'

Sandra enquired why.

'God knows! The Clean Air Act? Keeping all that smoke, soot and smog out of ageing lungs? Perhaps it's because Britain has at last discovered central heating, and moderated the national passion for hypothermia. Or perhaps it's eating more vitamin E? It works wonders for our Goddess of Love, Barbara Cartland.'

'I think it's the decline of religion,' decided Sandra solemnly, gazing through the window towards the sunlit spire of St Alphege's. 'Surely, if you don't believe in the blissful afterlife, you don't die as effortlessly as switching channels when you're bored with the programme you're watching?'

'It's sex,' Dr Lonelyhearts decided firmly. 'You live much longer if you put off having it till you're eighty. The principle was demonstrated by scientists in Canadian fruit flies.'

'Gives the flies something to look forward to, I suppose.'

'Of your ripe bunch, I'm only interested in Mr Harold Wooljohn.' Dr Lonelyhearts accepted another Glenlivet. 'The *Echo* said he's been smoking fifty a day for a hundred years – less, say, ten or twelve.'

I nodded. 'He puffs away at horrible little hand-rolled things like inflammable slugs, with strands of tobacco the colour of creosote dangling from each end.'

'Splendid!' Dr Lonelyhearts rubbed his hands. 'A good, tarry, unfiltered smoke. I must get him on the telly at the end of the month.'

I pointed out, 'Even if he was rolling pitch-pickled rope-ends, he wouldn't much serve as a government health warning at that age.'

Dr Lonelyhearts looked offended. 'Haven't you heard of my marathon? Up in London, last Sunday in July.'

I shook my head. 'I am growing a shade bored with marathons. I regard them as a mixture of hypochondria and hysteria. It's a fad equivalent to the medieval flagellants. They were an awful nuisance – in the thirteenth century you could hardly go anywhere without finding the streets choked with them. All flogging themselves till the blood ran, under

the impression it was doing them no end of good.' I con-
cluded, 'I've no quarrel with masochism, but I don't care for
it holding up the traffic.'

Dr Lonelyhearts disagreed. 'Twenty thousand people in
London and New York can't be wrong. Not if there's lots of
money in it. They reckon the Manhattan marathon is worth
five million dollars a year, and the TV ratings are magic. All
you need is a new angle. I've got one. It's a smoking
marathon.'

Sandra said, 'Oh, you mean a marathon for Stop Tobacco
Use, Britain!'

I remembered that Dr Lonelyhearts was their public
relations consultant – honorary, it was a better life-saving
cause than the lifeboats.

'No, I've left STUB!' he replied cheerfully. 'They are
worthy if guileless people, who like many do-gooders think
you can push the childish public around as you like, as a
nanny with a pram. The public are artful dodgers of dis-
agreeable facts. I've taken a public relations job with Freedom's Active Guardians – not at *all* honorary, I might tell
you.'

I frowned. In a world so busily living up to its acronyms, it
was as hard to identify a new one as put a name to a face in a
crowd.

He explained, grinning, 'FAGS is a harmless-sounding
front for the rich, ruthless, rapacious tobacco industry. And
it provides fat jobs for forceful people.'

I stared at him, shocked.

'How do you feel,' I enquired acidly, 'as the accessory to
the murder of 55,000 fellow-countrymen a year?'

Dr Lonelyhearts replied casually, 'The medical hierar-
chy's fierceness about smoking bears a fascinating resemblance to the Roman Catholic one's towards sex. Pleasures
which may both lead men into a disproportionate amount of
trouble.'

I told him indignantly, 'I have yet to see "sex" on a death
certificate.'

107

He reflected, 'Not a bad end, I suppose?'

I pointed out, 'But you've written articles telling people it's mad to smoke.'

'Of course. It's like walking to work along the railway lines. But I'm a professional communicator. I'm happy to let STUB! and FAGS battle for public opinion while I remain as uncommitted as Krupps, Vickers and the other thriving armourers. Public relations is a basic weapon of modern democracy,' he expanded.

'Of public misguidance,' Sandra ventured.

'You're perfectly right,' he agreed cheerfully. 'Do you suppose our politicians, royals, TV stars and general run of nobs are remotely like the images presented to the mob? We love or hate paper dolls. Polemics, like people, need expert display, Richard. Come to think of it, mine are the only battles won by camouflage.'

He finished his malt, looking smug.

'Did Jim Whynn turn all that stuff you mugged up on surrogate motherhood into a brilliant speech?' he asked.

I shrugged. 'He failed to catch the Speaker's eye.'

Sandra said when he had left, 'Dr Lonelyhearts is highly intelligent.'

I disagreed. 'You mean, too clever by half.'

She considered. 'No, by five-eights.'

15

I wandered into the warm, bright evening to cut back my cucumbers in the greenhouse.

'Richard!' Sandra was shouting from the back door. 'It's Sir Basil.'

I was enjoying his reflected gratitude. It was Jilly who had saved him from an unnecessary operation, by insisting to surgeon Bill Igtham that the violent stomach-ache on the eve of the Queen's Birthday might be psychological.

He was restlessly pacing the living room.

'Tio Pepe?' I suggested hospitably.

He tugged his beard violently. 'I'm terribly distraught this evening, Richard. I must succumb to Scotch.'

I poured him a Glenlivet.

'Your bloody Dr Lonelyhearts!' he complained angrily, gulping half a tumbler. 'You know I'm big in STUB!?'

I nodded.

'Now he's wrecking years of patient work by all of us, who've been informing the public that they're brainless nits to puff tobacco.'

He threw himself into an armchair.

'It's infuriating,' he continued warmly. 'The smoking statistics are the only cast-iron, copper-bottomed line we've got on the cause of cancer, which everyone is terrified of – and bloody rightly, too. The world should rejoice. Instead, it niggles. It quibbles and carps. It says it gets nervous and fat if it doesn't smoke. It pins its faith – its very life – on statistical flukes like your patient in the paper, Richard.'

He eyed me severely over his glass.

'Whom I should have been much happier had you left in the obscurity of his own foul fumes.' He confessed, 'After all these years of medical practice, human beings still baffle me,' adding grimly, 'I'm going to cripple his marathon.'

I asked how.

Sir Basil shrugged. 'God knows. He wants to show that smokers are as fit as non-smokers. It's criminal – it's murderous – the power, the money, the influence deployed by the capitalist Saracens against we band of Crusaders.'

He was also big in socialism.

'Suppose the capitalist sold baby food made with cheap, impure ingredients, which got them fat profits but killed their little customers every year in thousands?' He tugged the hairy lapel of his jacket. 'Possibly, I suggest, there might be some little fuss made in the newspapers? Slaughter them in their schooldays with smoke, and what happens? No one raises an adjective. "If blood be the price of advertising, their readers ha' paid it in full." Kipling.'

'Another malt?'

'How very kind. These murderous manufacturers go on about freedom of choice. Forsooth!' he continued to orate. 'Of course we should stay free to smoke or not. Entirely as we wish. We should stay free to chuck ourselves off Beachy Head. But the Eastbourne authorities offer bleak discouragement, paint warnings, put up barriers. Instead of suggesting it's a socially acceptable activity which makes teenagers sexy and as sophisticated as stuffed olives.'

It struck me, 'But how would the government raise the lost tobacco tax?'

'A tax on books.'

I was surprised. '*You*, suggesting a tax on culture?'

He raised his glass of whisky. 'No more than a tax on this is a tax on happiness. How are you off for honey?'

I admitted myself unable to give an offhand answer.

'You know I'm in Men of the Bees? You must have seen in today's *Echo* about that new high-tech apiary along Pilgrims' Way? Space-age beekeeping!' he said enthusiastically. 'Electronic hives, chemical feeding, it can produce honey of any flavour – mint, fruit-and-nut, salt-and-vinegar, butterscotch, pistachio nut. Did you know that honeycomb contains only half the calories of chocolate? Big opening in the slimmers' market. I've put several thousand quid of my savings into it,' he revealed proudly.

He gulped his Glenlivet and looked sheepish.

'Also, bees are environmental,' he said uneasily. 'And they're becoming a touch churlish with me in Meadowsweet. Muttering about people who get knighthoods on the backs of others who rescue jellyfish from radioactive water and dump lorry-loads of dung on government ministers' doorsteps at night. I'll send you a sample case,' he offered generously. 'We were working on a whisky flavour, but the bees only got pissed.'

As he left the telephone rang. It was Arthur Crevin, furious.

'Richard? Do you realize that you're the Godfather of the Methuselah Mafia? Those walking dead are organizing coach parties all round the county. If Fleet Street gets hold of the story, 100-year-olds will be flooding into Churchford like soccer fans. Probably cause as much disruption. It's now going to be tea and buns in St Alphege's parish hall.'

'Doctor,' Mrs Jenkins greeted me glumly before surgery the following morning. 'More trouble.'

'Still no suitable applicants?' I asked disinterestedly. Returning to the job, she was mystified at her performance of it for fifteen years without a fulltime assistant.

'Another runner in the Great Zimmer Walking-frame Stakes,' she announced morosely. 'A Mrs Emily Hitchey-Powell out at Trafalgar Cottage. She didn't make much sense on the phone, but she says she remembers meeting you during the Coronation.'

I called later that morning at a neat village house lying on the opposite side of Churchford from Jim Whynn's. There were rhodos in the garden and roses round the door. I pressed the bell in a well-polished brass plate. A long delay. Then shuffling inside, and the door slowly opened by an old lady.

'Congratulations!' I exclaimed pre-emptively. 'You've

111

been invited to the *Echo's* centurions' birthday party.'

'Actually,' she replied, 'I was phoning about mummy.'

'Ah,' I said.

'I'm only eighty-four,' she said apologetically.

'You don't look it,' I told her automatically.

'Mummy had me very young,' she explained.

She left me in a small, speckless room with delicate antique furniture and the scent of lavender. An animated porcelain figure in russet silk, perched on an embroidered armchair, greeted me, 'You doctors are so busy, I *do* so hate troubling you.'

I responded gallantly, 'Were only patients a fraction of your age a fraction as considerate.'

'But my young Sara,' Mrs Hitchey-Powell explained, 'utterly insisted. She truly is a scamp.'

I disagreed. 'I'm sure she's really a most responsible daughter.'

'Sara saw something in the paper about some sort of celebration or competition of interest to persons of my age.'

I asked what age it was.

'I'm 103, though I think it's a matter to keep quiet about, don't you, doctor?'

'You must join in the fun,' I insisted warmly. 'The editor's gathering lots of 100-year-olds for a wonderful champagne party at the Churchford Arms Hotel.'

'Ah, champagne!'

The look came into her delicate pink-and-white face of Cinderella recalling the ball.

'I haven't tasted a glass of the Widow – as we used to call it, *Veuve Cliquot*, you know – for simply ages. Not since the days of dear Romano's. *Dear* Romano's! In the Strand, as I'm sure you'll remember, doctor. Absolutely everyone went there, though it was rather *déclassé*, indeed quite *louche*. But such *fun*, with people like Oscar Wilde, such an *amusing* man, I do so wish I could remember the things he said, some were perfectly *killing*, I'm sure they'd still raise a smile if they were repeated even these days, though perhaps I'm thinking of someone else.'

She unexpectedly giggled like a tickled Gaiety girl.

'I was really quite a mettlesome filly when I was very young, you know, doctor. Dear mama and papa did not at all approve. Thank goodness Sara hasn't given me such trouble.'

I shifted uneasily on the bearskin rug. Her pale blue eyes gazed through the leaded window at the tiny close-cropped back lawn hedged with azaleas.

'The girls on the stage were – well, they were beautiful! The men in the stalls were most perfectly groomed . . .'

She turned her eyes on me.

'How strange, doctor, that one can remember some things perfectly clearly from one's youth, just as if one had learned a little song only yesterday, when one cannot some mornings remember if one has eaten one's breakfast or not. *We supped at Romano's, and all were most dutiful, We danced where gardenias have never yet bloomed . . .'*

There was silence. I wanted to blub.

She continued briskly, 'And who exactly will be at the party?'

'All sorts. The only qualification's having a 100-year-old birth certificate. A social mix from everywhere in southern England.' I thought of Rosie and Harold. 'Of course, it's dug up a few rough diamonds with hearts of gold.'

She considered. She drew a deep breath.

'Perhaps I should not like to mix with the sort of person you depict, doctor. Also I should need a new dress and we are rather awfully poor. Kindly tell the editor that I am unable to accept his most kind invitation because of a prior engagement.'

16

The front page of Saturday's national papers proclaimed that Sunday week's Smokers' Marathon had been banned from the streets of London.

The Home Secretary had struck. He had undergone passionate pressure from Mr Jim Whynn – 'the sex scandal MP' – who had outragedly declared it the most dangerous defilement of the capital since the Great Plague of 1665.

That afternoon I was playing golf with Dr Lonelyhearts.

'That bloody Barty-Howells,' he complained angrily, as we marched to the first tee. 'Getting this whoremongering psychopath of a crooked politician to grab a little cheap respectability for himself by undoing in half an hour my hard work of six months.'

He took a driver from his bag and whipped it savagely.

'I'd everything organized. The press from all over the world. All wildly interested in this unique sporting event – because of course they carry loads of cigarette advertising. I'd planned the route round London's famous pubs. Start at Ye Olde Cheshire Cheese in Fleet Street – handy for the hacks – end at the Prospect of Whitby in Wapping. All the runners would naturally be allowed to light up on the trot, so the entire world could see on TV that smoking is an utterly healthy activity.'

He glared at his ball as if looking Jim Whynn in the eye.

'Nicotine probably vastly improves athletic performance,' he suggested grumpily. 'It's a pity our pathetic lot at the last Olympics didn't slip a packet of twenty into their waistbands before getting on to the starting blocks. God! What a terrible shot.'

I teed up.

'My dear Aleyn, I sympathize with you,' I told him. 'Like a tender-hearted crocodile.'

'I can understand Barty-Howells,' he conceded. 'God knows why he wants to buy bees. He's enough in his bonnet to provide honey at ten to three into eternity. But Jim Whynn! Just my luck, I suppose. Grabbing the first chance to launder his filthy reputation.'

I objected, 'I happen to know that Jim has strong views against smoking. And politics is about people.'

'Politics is about politicians,' he corrected me. 'And God knows why there was such a fuss about one psychiatric report. I suspect there's 650 of them lying about somewhere.'

We started down the fairway.

'If that devious do-gooder Barty-Howells thinks he can get away with it,' Dr Lonelyhearts told me darkly, 'he's got a bigger surprise coming than Little Red Riding Hood.'

'Shall we double our usual stake on the round?' I suggested.

'No, I'm so upset I shall play terribly,' he pointed out sharply. *'And you bloody know it.'*

We finished the game. The club secretary greeted us irately in the locker room. He had been pestered all afternoon to get Dr Lonelyhearts to ring back urgently.

I disappeared into the bar, Dr Lonelyhearts into the telephone box. I was ordering my second Talisker when he reappeared. His mood was transformed. He looked as cheerful as Mickey Mouse.

'That was Sticks Cigarettes,' he announced excitedly. 'The managing director himself. You know their head office isn't in polluted London? It's set in the wholesome air of the Surrey countryside. The marathon is *on*. Sunday afternoon, as planned. We're running from Sticks HQ along the ancient twists and turns of Pilgrims' Way.'

He made an expansive flowing gesture.

'Across the delightful, photogenic slopes of the North Downs. And do you know where we'll end up, Richard?

Right here in Churchford. In the marketplace. Much healthier shots on TV,' he gloated, taking his gin-and-tonic from the barman.

He continued proudly, 'Did you know I'd already hired dozens of lovely girls to show almost their all while offering the runners free cigs every hundred yards? Now Sticks tell me that Old Mother's Gin and Fireball Scotch have swallowed my idea of a combined jollification, and are coming in with us. They're donating free booze for the girls to hand out as well.'

'Why don't the girls complete the contest by inviting the runners into the hedgerows?' I suggested. 'Chaucer himself would have thought of it.'

He laughed. 'I don't think you approve of our revels, Richard. You really are an old spoilsport. I just want everyone to have a good time. Think a moment – have you ever seen a picture of a marathon with anyone remotely enjoying himself?'

I had to agree.

I arrived home to find a Metro outside the front gate and Basil Barty-Howells in the living room having a Glengoyne with Sandra.

'Churchford!' he spluttered. He was red-faced with fury. 'Churchford! On my own hospital doorstep! I couldn't feel more insulted if Dr Lonelyhearts had deliberately puffed smoke in my face.'

'Oh, there's no danger of that,' I pointed out. 'He wouldn't dream of smoking. He knows it's far too dangerous.'

'I will not take this lying down,' continued Basil fiercely. 'I'll raise a saboteurs commando from STUB! Like wrecking the hunts.' His eye gleamed. 'Just like old days! How well I remember, when I was young with an anorak and an aerosol deodorant. I was blooded with the Quorn, you know. Those lovely crisp days of autumn! Those clear frosty ones of winter! Wherever in the world is more lovely than the superb English countryside, with the baying of hounds, the piercing

116

notes of the hunting horn, the comradeship of my fellows, the tasty picnics, the swigs from the flask . . . I've sabotaged them all, from John Peel's country in Cumberland right through the Kingdom to Mr Jorrocks' south of the Thames. They were the happiest days of my life,' he confessed smilingly. 'But of course a man has to give up blood sports when he's preoccupied with the demanding career of a consultant physician.'

I consoled him, 'Well, there'll be no horsewhips, and the pack is unlikely to bite.'

He looked doubtful. 'I won't get any recruits. We're too polite, too considerate, too meek, too non-aggressive, all us passionate non-smokers.'

'Like Hitler?' I suggested.

Jim Whynn enjoyed the pompous praise of newspaper editorials while Churchford became plastered with posters and festooned with flags heralding the junketing of two different death-defying groups.

The centurions' party started at noon on Saturday in the ballroom attached to Churchford's ancient coaching inn. It made the *danse macabre* look like the *cancan*.

Rosie Styles and Harold Wooljohn saw themselves as the Fred Astaire and Ginger Rogers of geriatrics, though their joint pose for the photographers was marred by Rosie remarking, 'TAKE YOUR BLEEDING HANDS OFF OF ME.'

'I rather fancy her,' Harold explained to me. 'Pity my bike's gone.'

I totted up that the guests of honour achieved the awesome total age of 3,502 years. Arthur Crevin buzzed among them shaking hands, the champagne was poured, the *canapés* circulated, the piping chatter rose, gasps greeted a vast *gâteau* wheeled in with 100 blazing candles.

'Ladies and gentlemen,' said Arthur. 'I have a sensational announcement.'

A small fat man I had never seen before stood beaming beside him.

'May I present Mr Lushington,' he continued delightedly. 'Chairman of Brighter Britain Ltd. Our premier provider of bingo halls, betting shops and similar places which make our country so exciting to live in.'

Arthur started clapping loudly. A few guests followed, looking blank, like dogs wagging their tails to please.

'I dislike the pompous title "senior citizen",' declared Arthur.

'So do I,' agreed Harold Wooljohn. 'I prefer to remain an ordinary dirty Dick.'

'So we have decided to call it the "Ancient Briton Award",' he announced unexpectedly. He produced a cheque. 'Mr Lushington has presented to our oldest guest today a prize of . . .' He hesitated impressively, waving it in the air with a cry of, '*Ten thousand pounds!*'

The news was flashed through the hearing aids, causing confusion.

'And the oldest,' proclaimed Arthur, 'is Mrs Irene Lambert of Himalaya Drive, who is 101. She wins over Mr Alfred Hosegood of Mons Avenue, who is also 101, by a fortnight.'

'By 0.04 per cent,' calculated Mr Lushington appreciatively. 'You don't see that sort of finish in the Olympics.'

The information slowly seeped in. There was more clapping. Mrs Lambert was a jolly lady, and had become instantly popular through her Marie Lloyd imitations.

'ARF A MINUTE!'

It was Rosie Styles. She was fiercely rummaging in her handbag. She extracted a long, tattered strip of paper.

'IT'S ME BIRTH CERTIFICATE,' she screeched. She waved it wildly. 'I'M 102.'

Arthur glared at her. 'Then why didn't you say so?'

'I FORGOT I WAS. I FORGOT I'D HAD MY 100TH BIRTHDAY. I FORGOT THE QUEEN'S TELEGRAM. OF COURSE, THAT'S WHY I DIDN'T GET ONE ON MY LAST BIRTHDAY,' she exclaimed. 'YOU CAN'T EXPECT PERFECT MEMORY AT MY AGE, CAN YOU?'

The room began to buzz. Arthur grabbed the birth certificate.

'Correction,' he declared hastily. 'Mrs Styles wins on a recount.'

'It's a proper shame,' objected Mr Hosegood indignantly. He was a tiny man with a long beard. 'She oughter be disqualified.'

'WHY SHOULD I?' Rosie demanded.

'Not giving your proper age to start with. You'd be disqualified from a baby show.'

'Come to think of it, I might be 102 as well,' speculated Harold Wooljohn. 'My father took a long time getting round to register my birth. He was a lazy bugger.'

I strode across to Arthur Crevin.

'Thank God I don't run a Tokyo paper,' he muttered to me. 'They've got them pushing 120 out there. They tell me that in Samarkand they're thicker on the ground than teenagers.'

I grabbed his arm.

'Stall for half an hour,' I commanded. 'Make a speech. Sing a song.'

He looked alarmed.'Why?'

'The winner isn't here at all.'

I jumped into my car and drove to Trafalgar Cottage.

'What a vulgar woman this Mrs Styles must be,' murmured Mrs Hitchey-Powell as I breathlessly reconstructed the scene. 'To be so brazen about money. Our generation really should try to preserve some dignity, these days when everyone seems to be applauded for behaving exactly as they like.'

I said pressingly, 'But ten thousand quid, Mrs Hitchey-Powell! It may not be the same as ten thousand quid in the times when you were dancing the night away at Romano's. But it would buy you a new dress or two.'

There was silence. She slowly folded her tiny hands on her lap.

'It's dreadfully sweet of you, doctor. I know how you

have my welfare at heart. But it would have made no difference had I attended the function. You see,' she confessed, 'I am only 100. A lady is entitled to lie about her age, surely?'

'Of course,' I assured her, puzzled. 'Though not often in that direction.'

She pursed her rosebud lips.

'You have forgotten young Sara,' she told me quietly. 'It would hurt her if everyone knew that I had her when I was just sixteen. Which is very, very naughty, isn't it? These days, anyway, so they tell me. But perhaps we weren't so strict when we danced where gardenias have never yet bloomed.' She whispered a sigh. 'Romano's, dear Romano's . . .'

I gulped.

I felt the next day's marathon would be an anticlimax.

The starting pistol was fired by a famous comic, miles away across the county boundary. The start was in late afternoon, giving the runners time for a comfortable Sunday lunch. It was a warm, clear day, with a breeze as refreshing as iced hock. I watched from Foxglove Lane on television.

The massed field in running gear made the Grand National look like a two-horse race. Delightedly smoking and sipping, flourishing at the cameras their give away cigarettes and plastic cups of booze, the competitors choked the lovely lanes winding among the unripe orchards, the plushy fields, the mellowing corn and authoritative oaks on the sunny side of the Downs.

That weekend I was on call for the practice. I was shortly summoned to a suspect appendix (it was wind). Driving home through the market place, I stopped to accept Dr Lonelyhearts' earlier invitation to the champagne tent, where he was emerging from a crowd of Sticks executives, looking nervous.

'You must be delighted with the turn out,' I congratulated him. 'Everything running well?'

He scowled. 'You're joking?'

'At the start, everyone looked as happy as a winner,' I stated.

'We've had five coronaries, and we aren't past Leatherhead.'

I expressed concern.

'God knows why some of these people entered. After all, it *is* an athletic event,' he was discovering belatedly. 'I suspect a lot of them have taken no more exercise than raising their hand to their mouth all their lives.'

He put his radio to his ear.

'Christ! Reigate Hospital has no more beds, and Redhill says it can't manage any more cases of alcohol poisoning.'

I left him, a worried general evacuating a wave of unexpected casualties.

In the early evening I was summoned to a choking child (tantrums). I stopped again in the market place. Dr Lonelyhearts was pacing frantically round the TV cameras.

'The Red Cross has opened an emergency station in Oxted,' he told me distractedly. 'The Department of Health is rushing a fleet of ambulances up the M20. There's a major catastrophe alert to every hospital in south-east England – if not a Civil Defence warning of imminent nuclear attack.'

I commiserated with him.

'Further, there're mass arrests for being drunk and disorderly in Dorking, in Westerham fifty of the idiots decided to pee together in the High Street, I'm expecting a delegation of residents any moment, followed on Monday by writs for moral outrage and the pollution of front gardens. Surely the first of the sober few will be here any minute?' He stared desperately past the brightly-flagged finishing line. 'At least, it'll make a reasonable TV picture on the news.'

We waited. The TV crews began to fidget. They gazed at the sky, they complained they had no lights. I looked at my watch.

'Why, it's past opening time. Perhaps they've all stopped at a pub for a drink?' I suggested, but he did not find it funny.

We waited longer.

121

Dr Lonelyhearts and his walkie-talkie exchanged agitated conversation. The TV crews packed up their cameras, loaded their vans and drove away. The Churchford street-lights came on. The Sticks executives made for their Rollses and Jaguars. They had not word nor glance for Dr Lonely-hearts. He sat head in hands on a packing case of filter-tipped.

'Where are they? Where are they?' he moaned, a general whose army had fled. 'Surely that happy multitude cannot in a few hours have vanished from the face of the earth? Even the San Francisco earthquake had survivors. Or is it going to be one of the great mysteries of history, like the *Marie Celeste*?'

I silently placed an arm round his shoulders. I left. The moon rose.

At home was Basil Barty-Howells, in the living room enjoying a Glenlossie with Sandra and covered with scarlet blotches.

'My savings – gone,' he announced happily. 'I loosed them from my hives into that sunken bit of Pilgrim's Way, just as it approaches Churchford. The last I saw of the marathon was it disappearing into the woods. It'll probably be there overnight. I don't know what it is about electronic hives,' he speculated, scratching himself, 'but they do seem to make the bees dreadfully hungry.'

He smacked his lips. 'This malt whisky is good stuff, thank God that unlike smoking you have to take a lot of it before it kills you. Yes, please, I'll have another.'

I encountered Dr Lonelyhearts in Churchford High Street three days later.

'I've been fired from FAGS,' he informed me dourly. He sighed. 'I should never have done the public relations for something I despised. "To thine own self be true." Shakespeare was perfectly right. But of course in his time hardly anyone but Sir Walter Raleigh smoked.'

17

Mrs Blessington for her annual check-up.

Torschlusspanik!

I knew it was now but a flicker of groundless alarm, like the fright cast upon a naughty child by a deceptive shadow.

I have been convinced for years that Mrs Blessington harbours a secret passion for me.

She always looks at me with the fascinated, awed but amused expression of a child enjoying the circus.

Whatever her clinical complaint, I shortly find myself listening to the sexual mechanics of her journey through life with Mr Blessington and occasional joy-riders. However peripheral her pains, she readily doffs her dress and generously strips off her boutique underwear to afford me a helpful view.

Mrs Blessington is fair with big eyes and a mouth which she maintains slightly open. She is tall, slim as a dart, with tits as neat as peaches. I regularly meet her socially at the Blessingtons' new, low, white house with swimming pool, floodlit patio and brick-built barbecue. Like many of my fellow guests, she politely feels the conversation best to hold my interest is about her ailments, often suggesting that we step upstairs to her bedroom where she can impart them more vividly. Her husband is in fast food.

A romance between doctor and patient has the pure, tragic beauty of classical love between unobtainables. The affair is unconsummative, unmentionable and preferably unnoticeable. Abelard and Héloise had it much easier.

It is strange – it is grotesque – how even middle-aged doctors excite women patients. I suppose we offer a mettlesome challenge to their seductiveness. This is obliged to triumph not as customary over wife, family and home, but over the entire General Medical Council as well.

'You're in lovely condition,' I smiled at her, unplugging my stethoscope from my ears.

'I'm so glad, doctor.' She reached for her coffee-and-cream lace bra. 'I'd hate anything to interfere with the summer production of the Churchford Mummers. At last little me has won the star part.'

I congratulated her.

'We're doing *Double Fault*,' she explained enthusiastically.

It was not a piece I recalled.

'You *must* come to the first night,' she insisted pressingly. 'It's in St Alphege's parish hall, just round the corner from you. We've already started rehearsing.'

To pass the time while she pulled on her white lace tights, I mentioned, 'In my youth I was thought by some a gifted amateur actor. As a houseman, I played many parts – Charley's Aunt, Captain Corcoran, Othello, all that.'

Her eyes shone brighter. 'But doctor, you must take a role! I'm sure there'll be no trouble, we're dreadfully short of talent with everybody away in August.'

I made depreciatingly disclaiming noises.

'Oh, but I absolutely insist, it would be enormously popular with the audience, and of course! We've just the part – The Doctor!'

I continued tutting.

'It's only a small part, take hardly any of your time,' she continued, fixing her earrings. 'You and I can have *enormous* fun together.'

I found I had agreed.

'I'm rather proud to be invited,' I explained it away to Sandra that evening. 'Surely you remember my flair upon the boards? The very first time you saw me was being Dick Whittington in the hospital panto. Or perhaps it was the cat.'

'Do what you like dear, but most men of your age and position in society exert themselves to avoid looking fools, not plunge head-first into it.'

I was hurt.

'The Mummers are perfectly respectable,' I protested. 'Sir Damian Havers is the President – though he wouldn't go nearer a performance than God drop into a front pew on Sunday morning.'

My first rehearsal was the following evening.

Double Fault was a thriller, set even before *The Moustetrap's* curtain had first risen. The action passed during Wimbledon week in the drawing room of a country house in Sussex. The plot revolved round the millionaire householder's faithless wife (Mrs Blessington) luxuriating in a secret affair with the Men's Singles Champion – in those days, Wimbledon champions not being all unruly teenagers.

The weather had turned freezing. I strolled to St Alphege's parish hall wondering if I might meet for the first time the man to conduct my daughter's wedding. Since my arrival in Churchford my neighbour in the vicarage was the Rev James Rumbold – a good man, fat and purple-faced, low church and low back pain. He had that summer retired to fish for trout in Devon during the fabled clerical longevity, expressing no impatience whatever for the delights he had extolled for fifty years of the life hereafter.

His replacement was the Rev Ron Flood, young, slim, angular, handsome, bushy-haired, trendy, left-wing, no dog collar and no-holier-than-thou. He was in the parish hall doorway, distractedly explaining that to heat it in August was contrary to parish regulations, if not the doctrines of the Church of England. His antagonist, muffled tightly in a mink coat, shivering and cross, was Mrs Noakes.

Mrs Noakes also had harboured a secret passion for me for some years.

'Doctor, how *lovely*!' exclaimed Mrs Noakes, throwing open her mink and clasping me to her black leotard while the Vicar instantly exploited the diversion to bolt into the church. 'And you're in the cast! We'll have enormous *fun* together.'

Mrs Noakes was short with black curly hair and a turned-up nose and tits tense as ripe aubergines. She lived in a vast 1930s mock-Tudor house, with no swimming pool but they had a villa in Fuengirola and a Rolls. My patients Mrs Blessington and Mrs Noakes were our magnificent rival hostesses, like Mrs Astor and Mrs Vanderbilt, Lady Cunard and Lady Londonderry, vying for the acclaim of Churchford society with wine and cheese.

She gripped my hand. 'Come and meet our dear producer. Here's our darling doctor.'

She introduced me to my bank manager.

I had already noticed Mr Wilbrahams keeping warm prancing about the bare stage in jeans and a flowery shirt saying things like, '*Adorable, lovely*, but just a teeny more *soul* in the flouting bit,' when he usually said things like, 'Your overdraft facility will of course be liable to our base rate plus three per cent.'

'Helen, *darling!*' He hugged Mrs Noakes. 'Your big scene is coming along *adorably*.'

'Lionel, sweet,' she murmured, patting one cheek and kissing the other.

'Helen, dearest!' exclaimed Mrs Blessington, appearing at the door in fishnet tights and fisherman's knit sweater and earrings like doughnuts.

'Valerie, *love*,' said Mrs Noakes, as they kissed one another.

The joy of amateur theatricals is the chance to act like actors, without the torment of making a living from it.

Mr Wilbrahams clapped his hands.

'Right, boys and girls, we'll go from the top,' he addressed the twenty or so lesser Mummers standing about the chilly hall. 'Act one, scene one, Helen and Valerie darlings, on stage.'

'My teeth are chattering so, I can't say my lines,' complained Mrs Blessington.

'You should have worn more dear,' suggested Mrs Noakes.

'Have you got thermal underwear under that black thing?' asked Mrs Blessington.

'I am *not* into thermal underwear, dear,' Mrs Noakes corrected her firmly.

'So sorry, Helen, perhaps you've been putting on a little weight,' Mrs Blessington apologized.

'Curtain up,' said Mr Wilbrahams.

'It's cocktail hour,' proclaimed Mrs Blessington loudly. 'Travers!'

'Coming, madam!' declared Mrs Noakes, appearing Right with both hands held upwards in front. 'Not too quick, Lionel, was it? I mean, I don't want to spoil the effect of my eavesdropping bit later on.'

'A well-trained maid would bring the *canapés* as soon as I ordered them,' said Mrs Blessington.

'A well-trained maid wouldn't be working in a dump like this,' said Mrs Noakes.

It was clear that Mrs Noakes did not care to bring Mrs Blessington's *canapés* at all, even in the cause of art.

'Let's go again, darlings!' called Mr Wilbrahams. He added softly to me in his bank manager's voice, 'Doctor, I've got a bit of an itching in the privates, could you take a look at it in the gentlemen's during coffee break?'

The Stage Manager, Mr Daypole (retail menswear), was shortly fussing, 'You stand here, Doctor. I do hope the real french windows won't stick on the night, like when we did *The Boy Friend*.'

Mr Deal (from the bookshop) arranged himself on the sofa. Mrs Blessington re-entered Right.

'Giles! My darling Giles! Surely not? He can't be dead? Travers!'

'Yes, madam.' Mrs Noakes entered Left, hands covering her face. 'The poor master! Only a minute ago he was laughing and joking as his wont.'

'You're certain you telephoned?' enquired Mrs Blessington.

'But here comes the doctor now,' imparted Mrs Noakes and removed her hands from her face.

I entered Centre through the imaginary french windows.

My performance was not demanding. I had to pronounce Mr Deal dead from natural causes. Mrs Blessington was later suspected of loading her husband with strychnine, conveniently disguised in the bitters lacing his morning gin.

'Something terrible has happened,' Mrs Blessington greeted me.

'Is he supposed to be dead?' I exclaimed.

'My God Mrs Horsefall I fear I am too late,' shouted The Prompter, Mrs Agnew (the building society).

'I mean, he doesn't look at all dead,' I stated.

Mr Dale was crestfallen. 'I've been practising ever so hard at home, Doctor. I swear I've trained myself to hold my breath a whole ten minutes on end.'

'That may be the trouble,' I assisted him. 'Corpses have their mouths open and floppy like this.'

'Oooo, doctor, don't!' cried Mrs Noakes, covering her face with her hands again.

No one could argue, as I was an accepted corpse expert. Mr Wilbrahams suggested I rehearsed Mr Deal in private.

'Should I kiss the doctor?' asked Mrs Blessington.

'Why?' demanded Mr Wilbrahams.

'To show my relief.'

'I think a peck on the cheek would do,' Mr Wilbrahams said uncertainly as Mrs Blessington took my head in both hands and impacted a kiss on my mouth.

'Your husband's corpse isn't cold,' Mrs Noakes said censoriously.

'It makes me look more suspicious,' Mrs Blessington informed her. 'Shall we do it all again?'

'I think the coffee's ready,' said Mr Wilbrahams.

In the gents, Mr Wilbrahams dropped his trousers and I diagnosed *tinea cruris*.

'It's only athlete's foot of the crotch,' I reassured him cheerfully.

'I was naturally most concerned, doctor,' he muttered. 'Though I live a blameless life.'

'It used to be called dhobi itch – caught from the washing, you know, when India was the jewel in the crown. I can give you some tablets.'

'Such a relief, doctor,' he said gratefully. He hesitated. 'It makes a man feel *unclean* talking to someone like Mrs Blessington.'

Outside waited The Colonel, Mr Collingwood (insurance), who wondered if I could look at the lump on his back. Before leaving I ordered from The Box Office, Mrs Fenwick (teacher at the Beowulf Comprehensive), two dozen seats for the opening night.

'Giving free seats to watch yourself in the pillory,' commented Sandra tartly, 'strikes me as the height of exhibitionism.'

I decided that she was jealous of Mrs Blessington.

18

For our rehearsal the following evening I brought my son Andy's textbook of forensic medicine. I felt it would not be enormously helpful to Mr Dale. The colour photographs on every page were mostly of Body After Two Weeks in Sea, Charred Remains of the Pilot, Decomposition with Maggots in Mobile Home and Removal of Stomach Contents with Stainless Steel Ladle.

He stared pop-eyed, also at Sodomy with Violence, Routine for Rape and Great Variations in the Breasts.

'I'm sure on the night you'll look as dead as a doornail,' I encouraged him.

'I'll go on practising at home, doctor,' he agreed earnestly. 'Though the wife says it's getting on her nerves. She tells me she hopes when I *do* kick the bucket I'll look more presentable, or it'll put off the relatives.'

When I entered through the french windows Mrs Blessington implanted a lingering kiss.

'Valerie, darling,' suggested Mr Wilbrahams nervously, 'the audience will begin to lose the thread of the plot.'

'But aren't I a passionate woman?'

He shrugged his shoulders. He was the miserable *maestro* handling a touchy *prima donna* liable to sweep out at any moment, also to move her bank account elsewhere.

I shortly feared that Mr Wilbrahams was losing his grip on his company. The Wardrobe Mistress, Mrs Ellison (Robbins Modes), threatened to quit because Mrs Blessington wanted to find Mr Dale dead wearing a bikini – 'I could *easily* have been in the pool' – and Mrs Noakes wanted a uniform of black miniskirt with frilly knickers – 'It's the *period*, dear.' The Village Bobby, Mr Harcourt-Lumsley (actuary), having no dialogue declared his part needed playing for laughs like the Keystone Cops, and kept bending his knees and pinching Mrs Noakes' bottom.

The weather turned stifling, the Rev Ron Flood apologized for the immovable windows, which did not seem to have been opened during the Rev James Rumbold's long incumbency. The Prompter drew me aside and confessed a burning sensation round her kidneys. Finding nothing abnormal in the dressing room, I invited her to bring a specimen to rehearsal.

I had generously distributed my dozen pairs of tickets among the local medical fraternity, ten of whom responded they would absolutely love to come but were most unfortunately on call that night. Churchford seemed the best protected community medically in the country. Dr Quaggy accepted. I knew he was too mean even to refuse a drug rep's ballpoint.

'But you complain all week when you've had to buy him a drink in the golf club,' Sandra remarked.

'It's worth it. I shall have great pleasure watching him listen to the thunderous applause I receive from my fellow-citizens. Bumbly Bill Hawesbury's coming.' He was Churchford's senior and most lethal GP. 'He says anything's preferable to watching that cretinous rubbish every night on television.'

'You know Jim Whynn's going?'

I nodded. 'I saw in the *Echo* he would be attending the Mummers' latest production because he was of course passionately interested in the Arts, which received generous subsidies from a government which placed the national culture even before the national economy.'

'I bet he gets out of it. Now he's got the item in the local paper.'

'God knows what I shall do with the rest of the tickets,' I told her gloomily. 'An empty first two rows in the stalls will look as though the audience is frightened of catching something from us.'

131

Dress rehearsal!

Real french windows. I was puzzled at The Prompter shadowing me about the stage clutching a rolled-up copy of *Country Life*.

'I come from the service of a duchess, madam,' observed Mrs Noakes, flouncing her knickers in Act One. 'Don't you think I should stress the *duchess*, Lionel? To show I've come down in the world, working for her?'

'But Helen darling you did it beautifully,' murmured Mrs Blessington. 'You sounded *real* working-class instead of trying to assume a posh accent.'

'*Thank you*, Valerie,' said Mrs Noakes icily.

The off-stage plot was the more interesting. Mrs Noakes, whose husband was in fitted bathrooms and kitchens, came from a semi-det against the railway lines and went to the Beowulf Comprehensive. Mrs Blessington was raised among rhododendrons and tennis-courts and achieved O-levels at St Ursula's independent. As they were too grand to mix with ordinary Mummers, they had been sharing a dressing room for a fortnight and getting on each other's nerves.

'Furthermore, Valerie, I *should* know how maids speak, having employed them in my time.'

Mrs Blessington agreed readily. 'Yes, darling, from agencies by the evening.'

'As a consideration for my guests,' snapped Mrs Noakes. 'Not like some dinner parties I could mention when the husband is awash with martinis and ladles duck gravy all down the front of a brand new dress.'

Mrs Blessington glared. 'You know perfectly well our cheque was in the post in the morning.'

'Exactly! For about half the price.'

'Oh, really?' enquired Mrs Blessington indifferently. 'We thought you'd bought it in a sale.'

Mrs Noakes rasped, 'I will have no further part in this childish charade,' and swept off stage to her Rolls.

Mrs Blessington shouted, 'Thank God for that selfish exhibition of disgusting manners! I've been absolutely long-

132

ing to get out of performing in this incredibly stupid play,' and swept off stage to her Mercedes.

Mr Wilbrahams stood ashen-faced, as though confronting single-handed an armed raid on his bank.

Medicine teaches you to think on your feet. I caught them in the car park.

I soothed them that all artistic persons were sensitive – Garbo, Liz Taylor, Pamela Stephenson – and that The Show Must Go On was dogma as binding as the Hippocratic Oath. They were already more furious with themselves than with each other. They would have hated to miss an event which rendered vanity tolerable and sexiness shameless, and for which they had bought expensive new clothes. They instantly fell into a tight embrace, shed profuse tears and declared how lovely the other was.

We returned to Act One. The Prompter was still following me about with *Country Life*. When I entered through the french windows Mrs Blessington looked at me dreamily and gave me another lingering kiss. Mrs Noakes also gave me a lingering kiss, still holding the *canapés*. Mr Wilbrahams stared glassy-eyed, like the captain bravely on the bridge with the rest of his beloved ship already under the waves. As I exited, The Prompter slipped into my hands from cover of *Country Life* a jam jar of urine.

When I got home Sandra said, 'Oh, I managed to get rid of those unwanted tickets. Jilly's organizing a party of housemen from the General. Your supporters' club filling the first two rows of the stalls should stop you getting stage fright.'

My heart fell. I remembered from my own houseman days that, unlike the West End critics, they express displeasure with piercing remarks of 'What a load of crap', and 'Christ, let's get out of this before the pubs shut'.

First night!

I peered excitedly through the curtain while the Church-ford Public Library Quartet performed a selection of favourite overtures in the orchestra pit. Bumbly Bill Hawesbury was in the second row, asleep already. Sandra and Jilly sat among a dozen or so young men and women who were exhibiting a light-hearted approach to the evening by folding the programmes for paper darts. Dr Quaggy's seats were empty. The Stage Manager tapped me urgently on the shoulder.

'Message from Mr Whynn. He's unable to be present. Unexpected meeting in Downing Street with the Prime Minister.'

First-night adrenalin had restored Mr Wilbrahams to his happier self, jumping about in dinner jacket with light blue frilly shirt and purple satin bow tie, kissing our two leading ladies as they emerged from a dressing room resembling a prosperous florist's, and inviting everyone to the after-theatre champagne party, which I happened to know was the supermarket sparkling Samur party.

The Public Library Quartet scraped to a halt. The house lights dimmed. The stage lights brightened. 'Oh, dear,' exclaimed The Stage Manager, 'I can't get the curtain up.'

Mr Wilbrahams, The Electrician young Mr Fignall (Ritzy Video Hire) and myself tugged on the rope. It gave, the curtain shot up like a camera shutter. It revealed Mr Dale in knickerbockers and a Norfolk jacket with his back to the audience peering skywards.

Thunderous applause.

Mr Dale turned with a sickly grin and opened the play by raising the significant glass of gin-and-bitters to implant it in the audience's mind.

'Cheers!' called someone in the house.

Loud laughter.

Inspector Dogged, Mr Attwell (landlord, The Three Feathers), entered Left.

Thunderous applause. Also whistles and cries of, 'Your last orders, please!'

Mr Dale and Mr Attwell pickaxed the foundations of the plot with a conversation about the recent strange behaviour

134

of Mrs Blessington. Mr Attwell exited Left and Mrs Blessington entered Centre.

Thunderous applause.

Mrs Blessington enquired about the whereabouts of the *canapés*, brought Right by Mrs Noakes.

Thunderous applause.

Mrs Blessington and Mrs Noakes exited. Mr Dale at last sipped his gin-and-bitters, made a noise like faulty heavy machinery and threw himself on the sofa with staring eyes, gaping mouth and spreadeagled limbs, looking as dead as ever achieved by any corpse I had encountered.

I was waiting in the wings, butterflies in stomach.

Through the canvas scenery, Mrs Blessington was distractedly commanding Mrs Noakes to send for the doctor. The Stage Manager was nervously jerking at the rope which controlled the curtain. There was a whoosh and a sandbag dropped from the flies to hit The Electrician on the head. Under the horrified gaze of The Scene Shifters, Mrs Timberlyn (supermarket management), and Mr Angus (estate agent), he fell to the floorboards pale and senseless, looking even more dead than Mr Dale on public view a few feet away.

'My God, I've killed Ernest,' cried The Stage Manager.

'Shhhhhh!' hissed The Prompter.

I sprang to The Electrician's head. Still breathing. Pulse regular. Concussion.

'He's still alive,' I assured everyone.

'The doctor is coming as quickly as he can, madam,' I heard Mrs Noakes saying shrilly a yard from my right ear.

'He seems an absolute age, Travers,' observed Mrs Blessington in a similar tone, which indicated vexing distraction from their parts by the unexpected whoosh and thud backstage.

Mr Wilbrahams grabbed my arm.

'You're on!' he hissed.

I hissed back, 'I've got to attend my patient.'

He hissed frenziedly, 'Do you want to wreck the show?'

I hissed severely, 'Do you want to kill the patient?'

'The doctor is coming as quickly as he can, madam,' Mrs Noakes continued to inform Mrs Blessington, who repeated the observation, 'He *still* seems an absolute age, Travers.'

Mr Wilbrahams hissed maniacally, 'Get on, get off, and *then* stop him dying.'

I hissed threateningly, 'Oh? You want me to commit manslaughter?'

'The doctor *must* be coming as quickly as he can,' screeched Mrs Noakes.

'He seems an absolute *eternity*, Travers,' agreed Mrs Blessington hysterically.

I had an idea. 'Get a doctor!' I hissed.

I stepped through the french windows with my bag.

Thunderous applause.

'But here comes the doctor now,' perceived Mrs Noakes.

It brought the house down.

I was puzzled. I knew I was good, but I did not know I was that good. Listening to the cheers, clapping, whistling and someone shouting, 'Late as usual!' it came to me that for a local doctor to play the local doctor was a mistake.

The noise lessened. I was about to pronounce Mr Dale dead from natural causes when Mrs Blessington confusedly skipped half a page and locked me in an embrace.

Thunderous applause. Except from Sandra, I noticed.

Wriggling free, I asked, 'God! What's happened to your husband?'

The line went over tremendously.

Mrs Noakes confusedly kissed me. Mrs Blessington kissed me again. Mr Deal sneezed. The house was now like Comics' Gala Night at the Palladium. Though still except for Sandra.

I was surprised to see Bumbly Bill Hawesbury appearing through the french windows bumbling, 'Where's the patient?'

Mr Deal leapt from the sofa, exclaiming in alarm, 'I'm only *pretending* to be dead, Dr Hawesbury.'

Mrs Blessington and Mrs Noakes kissed Bill Hawesbury.

Dr Quaggy entered left, asking briskly, 'What's the trouble? I've only just walked into the place.'

Mrs Blessington kissed Dr Quaggy. Two young men climbed on the stage announcing they were surgical house officers from the General, and could they join the party? Dr Quaggy said angrily, 'Is this some sort of schoolboy joke, Richard? I really do not expect such conduct from a fellow GP.'

I said, 'Ah, well, that's show business.'

I had the freakish feeling that he reminded me of somebody else.

Dr Quaggy continued irately, 'I was told there was a man seriously ill. I pride myself on my sense of humour, but I regard all this as deplorable taste.'

He noticed Mr Deal, who had resumed mortality on the sofa.

'Ah, there's the case. Right, who's going to perform the cardiac message? I'll administer the kiss of life.'

'Don't touch me, I feel fine! I remember all those scary pictures.' Mr Dale leapt off the sofa and exited Centre, colliding with Inspector Dogged, who declared, 'It's all right, I've phoned for an ambulance,' to shouts of 'Time, please!'

The house was now like the Kop with Liverpool scoring the equalizer. Except for Sandra.

Mrs Noakes advanced blazing-eyed to the footlights. 'You ungrateful buggers!' she spat at the audience.

The two young doctors were kissing Mrs Blessington. Mr Wilbrahams appeared through the french windows in his shirt-sleeves, announcing that he could not lower the curtain because the sandbag was part of the mechanism but money would be returned at the box office.

I found The Electrician sitting up and shaking his head in the arms of The Prompter. I drove behind the ambulance to the General and left him recovering in the accident and emergency department. I drove back to Foxglove Lane. Sandra was in the living room. A bottle of Talisker and a glass stood on the table. I asked her how she enjoyed the show.

'You were magnificent,' said Sandra quietly.

I stared.

'You were the only one who didn't look cross or flustered, darling. Just miserable.'

I gulped the Talisker. 'Did absolutely everyone want their money back?'

'Not a single one. Though I think it was only because the whole audience had been given free seats by the cast. That's why the fiasco was so sad. However awful the Mummers, isn't amateur dramatics really working hard to give a party for your friends? And what's more heartbreaking than a party which flops?'

I agreed. Mrs Noakes' final line was among the most heartfelt uttered upon the boards. I added off-handedly, 'I can't understand why Mrs Blessington and Mrs Noakes kept kissing me.'

'I can,' Sandra decided. 'After all, you were the father figure in the cast. I've often noticed how those two – like a lot of women in the practice – look upon you with an amused and tolerant affection. Why, it's like your own daughter Jilly.'

I sighed. *Torschlusspanik!*

19

Torschlusspanik!

Within a month my own daughter Jilly will be a married woman.

'Shouldn't we do something about it?' I asked Sandra anxiously over breakfast. 'Get a marquee for the garden, that sort of thing? Though God knows why the middle class should want it to look more like a circus than it is.'

'I've ordered it. Also chosen the guests and printed the invitations.'

'Oh? Well, I'm utterly content restricting my parental importance to signing the cheques and choosing the champagne.'

'That's a relief. You seem to have been so awkward about everything recently.'

Jilly appeared downstairs. She was spending her few days' leave at Foxglove Lane, delighted to be moving from the stark resident doctors' quarters at the General to the flat they had found on the south edge of London. Peter had averted the prospect of speedy divorce by rising to senior registrar at the famous Royal Women's Hospital in Chelsea. He seemed likely to scale the golden gynaecological ladder faster and higher than his father. I already proudly saw headlines SIR P. TAVERILL AT THE PALACE THE NATION WAITS.

'It'll be so convenient for both of us, even on call,' Jilly was saying, pouring coffee.

I became the heavy father over the top of *The Times*. 'You're serious about continuing your career? Despite medicine causing more problems in marriage than money?'

She answered spiritedly, 'I'm not going to end up just as a doctor's wife, oh, sorry mum.'

'Not at all,' murmured Sandra.

'After all, the NHS is generous with its maternity arrangements.'

'It's got no choice,' I snorted. 'With the British medical profession rapidly becoming as female-dominated as the Russian one.'

'Though the only fair way to equalize the sexual chances,' she pointed out, 'is forcing all the rising young lads to take nine months' holiday for two or three years running. I must get the honeymoon fixed,' she continued with surgical efficiency. 'We're going to Greece, nothing like culture. And fix the Vicar. Do you suppose he'll mind us arriving for the wedding from the same address? I hear he's more broad-minded than old Rumbold, who thought Hell yawned for anyone parking in the grass round the churchyard.'

Sandra sighed. 'When your father and I got married, my parents became very upset about premarital intercourse – didn't they, dear?'

'I can't remember,' I told her. 'Either occasion.'

'What do you tell any young patients who ask?' Jilly said curiously.

'That it doesn't matter in the slightest if they copulate after or before or even during the ceremony.'

'Saves a lot of fuss,' Jilly agreed.

'So I'm married to a man with no morals?' said Sandra.

'Oh, morals are a most unreliable guide to what's right or wrong,' I told her. 'So many people muddle them up with their prejudices. I say, look at this!' I pointed to *The Times'* front page. 'The Ministry's shutting down our Dower House Hospital. It's been leaked.'

'The Dower? It's got a lot of local sympathy,' Jilly commented doubtfully.

'Utterly misplaced,' I disagreed. 'It's inconvenient, inaccessible and insanitary. I know it's a lovely Georgian mansion in rolling parkland, but most patients are put into one of the annexes behind which date from World War Two – if not World War One. Its only recommendation is looking

140

less like Dartmoor than the General. It would be condemned as an unhealthy slum, if it wasn't inhabited only by unhealthy people.'

'All the same, tucked away in the Dower are half the General's paediatric beds,' Jilly said crisply. 'And as far as the Health Service is concerned the Dower House is simply part of the General, even at the opposite end of an awkward bus route.'

Sandra looked pensive. 'Wasn't it Churchford Cottage Hospital before the NHS took over?'

I nodded. 'Where GPs did terrible things. Tonsils and adenoids and appendices and hernias and other operations we were no more fitted to perform than the Mummers to perform at the National Theatre.' I rose, glancing at the kitchen clock. 'Nye Bevan is never sufficiently credited with improving the national health by rendering the GPs harmless.'

'Good morning, doctor. I see the Dower House is going,' Mrs Jenkins greeted me at the surgery.

'Quite the most sensible official decision since they dispatched Florence Nightingale to the Crimea.'

'Mr Blackadder's already in your consulting room. It's his knee. And will you call on Mr Whynn? He's got a cough and a temperature and he's rather worried it might be something nasty, as he got back only last night from a trip to the Gulf. At the taxpayers' expense, doubtless.'

Douglas Blackadder had not really come about his knee. He had come about Annabel.

'Did you know she was released from that terrible place last Friday?'

I frowned. 'No! I saw nothing in the newspapers.'

Douglas sighed. 'I'm afraid they've lost interest in her. It's like last year's pop star, isn't it? She feels the world's been rather hard on her for being silly for just a day or two. Now she's paid for it, she'd like to tell the world as much.'

'Fleet Street may forget her, but Jim Whynn won't,' I told him warmly. 'He promised he'd issue a statement to the press saying that all was forgiven. Which would help her to get a job.'

'That would be wonderful,' exclaimed Douglas, looking relieved. 'She just wants to draw a line through her life and start afresh. She certainly needs ordinary down-to-earth work. Otherwise, I'm frightened she may fall prey to any political organization which wants to exploit her, and maybe end up in an even worse mess.'

I asked guardedly. 'Had prison any dire effect on her?'

He smiled faintly. 'Only a Cockney accent and the habit of guarding all her possessions at home lest they're instantly pinched.'

Later that morning, I found Jim Whynn suffering from acute bronchitis but cheerful. He sat in the circular sitting room wearing jersey and slacks, coughing amid piles of folders and papers. I reassured him on the absence of signs indicating mysterious Middle Eastern diseases and politely asked after Charlotte.

'She's out doing a little discreet canvassing. You know she's hoping to get a seat on the local Family Practitioner Committee?'

I looked surprised. Jim laughed. 'She'd be your boss, Richard. Terribly important to me, having her in a respectable and powerful local job. She doesn't know the first thing about medical practice, of course. But neither do any of the ministers when they're appointed to run the entire Health Service.'

I wished her luck, adding, 'About that committee job you promised me. I really would like it, you know. My daughter's to be married in little over a fortnight, and it's concentrated my mind wonderfully. I don't want to continue practising medicine till I die, but if I don't continue doing useful work I'd kill myself.'

He looked faintly uneasy. 'I've rather distanced myself from the health people. Between you and me, I've been vaguely offered a job some time or another in the Department of Transport.'

I congratulated him.

'I'll see old Forditch, and do my best,' he promised. 'There shouldn't be any problem. Yes, Transport really is good news,' he reflected seriously. 'A notch on the greasy pole.'

I said, 'I see the Government's furthering the medical care of Churchford by shutting one of its hospitals.'

'Oh, we've thrown that to the moles, have we?' he asked lightly. 'Always better to break these things unofficially. Then we can get out of them if the fuss isn't worth it.'

I warned him, 'Churchford's going to run a political fever, you know. Closing any hospital anywhere always causes it. An unnecessary complaint, our hospitals being as comfortably plenteous as our pubs.'

'Bertie Bullivant made anything of it yet? Slow off the mark. A slack politician.'

'He's only just heard of it,' I excused him.

'No, we did a deal about the Dower House weeks ago, over dinner,' Jim informed me. 'I offered Bertie a juicy local issue to exploit if he'd keep quiet about the new motorway we're planning, cutting through the working-class estate on the London road.'

'But that would cause enormous uproar,' I said in alarm. 'The houses have just been built.'

'These minor embarrassments are always likely when roads are planned by the Department of Transport and towns by the Department of the Environment,' said Jim airily. 'The unions will become dreadfully upset, and quite rightly. But Bertie recognizes like anyone else with sense that a short cut to the future Channel tunnel is vital to British industry. So between us we've done the country a load of good. The co-operation between government and opposition is a great strength of British politics.'

'And you're shortly to get a job in the Department of Transport?'

'Yes, though naturally I didn't mention that to Bertie.'

I handed him a prescription. 'Young Annabel Blackadder was out of jail last week.'

'Thank God that affair seems to have blown over,' he said feelingly.

I reminded him, 'You *did* say you'd help her get a fresh start in life.'

He looked surprised. 'When she all but wrecked my own?'

'But everything ended reasonably well for you.'

'Only because I gave the Prime Minister a splendid excuse to sack a stupid Minister.'

I said uneasily, 'Annabel's paid pretty heavily.'

'Personally, I think she should have been put inside for much longer. We're far more leaked against than leaking. How does the public expect to be governed efficiently when it knows exactly what the government's going to do to it?'

I left saddened. I wondered if Churchill ever abandoned his principles so readily.

Sandra was with Jilly in London shopping for wedding dresses and suchlike. I reached home after evening surgery to find her in the living room surrounded by expensive parcels.

I poured myself a Lagavulin.

'Shutting Dower House is going to be the biggest sensation in Churchford since the rural dean tried to murder his wife,' I told her. 'I've had Quaggy on the phone three times telling me how all the GPs are outraged.'

'But there's a perfectly good mothers and babies unit at the General already,' Sandra said absently, unwrapping.

'Yes, and now the Health Service will save money by closing Dower House to expand it. But people always become indignant about mothers and babies. They're among the few uncontaminated items of our society, like Harry Secombe.'

The doorbell rang. It was the Rev Ron Flood.

'I saw your car passing, doctor, and there's something I'm terribly anxious to talk about. As Jilly told me about the wedding this morning, I felt I could drop in for a chat.'

I was irritated by the visitation, but hospitably offered a drink.

He smiled. 'People *always* offer clergymen sherry, but I'd much prefer some of that whisky. Doctor, you and I could do great things together in Churchford.'

'Good,' I said.

Sandra cleared the shopping to make space for the Rev Ron Flood on the sofa. He wore an open pink shirt and jeans and was shod with sandals, like the apostles. The Rev James Rumbold wore all seasons the same heavy dark suit with clerical collars which cover the years of our acquaintance grew softer and yellower, as his teeth.

'Doctor, are you a practising Christian?' the Rev Ron Flood enquired earnestly.

'I'm a Voltairian.'

He looked puzzled.

' "If God did not exist, it would be necessary to invent him",' I quoted. 'Supposing we have invented him? Would it make the slightest difference to our behaviour, worship or spiritual solace? Does it matter if God created the world or it's a colossal accident?'

'If you'll excuse me, doctor, I don't feel inclined at the moment for deep theological discussion. My predecessor – a more conventional clergyman than I am – gave me only one item of pastoral advice. Never become involved in arguments about the existence of God.'

Sandra asked, 'Are you quite comfortable in the vicarage, Mr Flood? I mean, all by yourself?'

'Perfectly. I live as simply as a goldfish.' He turned to me eagerly. 'An idea has been growing in my mind since I discovered we were neighbours. Co-operation between the Church and medicine. After all, it's an historic one. Jesus was a healer.'

I agreed. 'He was very good on leprosy.'

'You know the Bishop of Hindchester?'

'The health buff?'

He nodded vigorously. 'He says that half the patients of any GP are suffering from spiritual and not bodily afflictions. Anxiety, stress, guilt, all that.'

145

'Oh, I agree.'

'And these are problems which the average doctor can spare only about five minutes apiece to solve.'

'I entirely agree.'

He added perkily, 'Why not send them to the vicar? I'm sure that a quiet, unburdening chat with me would have the same effect as a prescription for tranquillizers.'

'I agree perfectly,' I said, rising and hoping to get rid of him.

'Would you care for another whisky, Mr Flood?' invited Sandra.

'How very kind.'

When he left after a second Lagavulin, Sandra complained, 'You were ridiculously pompous to that nice young man.'

'Everyone becomes pompous when talking to clergymen or headmasters. Haven't you noticed?'

'Anyway, doctors are more inclined to behave like God than believe in him,' she said sharply.

' "Where there are three doctors there are two atheists." They were already saying it in Latin.'

'*You* don't believe in God.'

'Yes, I do. He resembles a very decent but rather testy old member of the golf club, with a beard.'

'I wonder why the vicar isn't married?' Sandra speculated. 'He's got a perfectly good house and job.'

'As Jane Austen would say today, "It is a truth universally acknowledged, that a single man in possession of a good fortune, must be as queer as a Masons' handshake." '

'You really are becoming quite as uncharitable as a traffic warden,' she accused me. 'The vicar was trying hard to be helpful, and you weren't giving him the slightest encouragement.'

I explained, 'We doctors have a traditional suspicion of the Church. Both of us have the admirable aim of preserving human happiness, but we take people as they are while they

– being understandably other-worldly – take them as they ought to be.

'There you go again,' exclaimed Sandra. 'Pompous.'

I countered resignedly, 'It's the preferable vice of middle age. Unlike vanity, bigotry or meanness it incites only amusement.'

'Why *don't* you send him your neurotics?'

'My God, If I did! The poor bugger wouldn't be left time to pee, let alone pray.'

20

My first patient the following morning was Mrs Gladwin. She was a demure, slim blonde in a plain blouse and dark skirt with anxiety, headaches and palpitations. She wanted more Valium.

I automatically reached for my prescription pad, asking, 'You're really feeling less worried since you've been on these capsules?'

'I am, but my husband isn't. He's getting quite worked up, doctor. About me being hooked on tranquillizers for the rest of my life. Besides, I get so drowsy in the afternoons – you know I work part-time as his receptionist? Why, I'm yawning in the clients' faces.'

Mr Gladwin was a partner in a well-rooted firm of Churchford accountants with offices above the shops in the High Street.

I asked, 'Are you a good Christian?'

She looked startled. 'Well, I got married in a church.'

'I'm sure your case would benefit from seeing the vicar of St Alphege's.'

'What's he know about it?' she asked sharply.

'Your symptoms may possibly be due to the turmoil in your soul, Mrs Gladwin.'

She drew a breath. 'Go on.'

'And we all know how the mind affects the body, don't we?'

She nodded, looking blank.

'The vicar may be able to soothe you with an understanding chat. It would save you taking a lot of powerful drugs which upset your husband and give a dreadful impression to his clients and distress the Government with their cost.'

She objected, 'It doesn't seem right, taking a headache to a vicar.'

'The Church has been doing this sort of thing for ages,' I reassured her. 'Why, he might perform a miracle. Anyway, it can't do any harm.'

'I suppose it'll be something to pass the time,' she agreed dubiously.

Overnight I had begun to think more warmly of the Rev Ron Flood's offer. It would be a way of giving my tedious patients and myself a holiday from one another. I usually effected this by sending them to Walter Elmsworthy at the General, but a clergyman unlike a psychiatrist cost the NHS nothing. And after all, the vicar was like myself a professional man. The only difference was his work being totally unimpeded by the death of the patient.

Next morning's surgery brought Mrs Vince. She was a divorced, plump redhead who ran the Dingley Dell Coffee Shop in the High Street. She had anxiety, headaches and palpitations. She wanted more Valium.

'Can't you pep up the dose, doctor?' she asked cheerfully. 'I like it, I like it!'

I automatically reached for my prescription pad, but hesitated.

I asked, 'Are you a good Christian?'

'We've got a box for the Children's Fund.'

'Would you like to see the vicar of St Alphege's?'

'Why?'

'These capsules aren't chockies, you know. You don't want to be hooked on them for the rest of your life. He might be able to sort out your problems with a good heart-to-heart.'

She gave a slow, speculative smile. 'Can't say I've ever had one with a vicar before.'

'I assure you that the Church is as eager to ease the world's stress as the credit card companies to lend it money.'

'I'll give anything a whirl once,' she agreed, laughing. 'And I *must* get rid of these headaches, doctor. My boyfriends do seem to find me so boring when I've got them.'

After surgery I stopped at the General for the laboratory investigations I had wanted on the germs invading Jim Whynn's chest. In the car park I recognized my patient Syd Farthingale, shop steward of the Association of Confederated Health Employees, haranguing the mob – a disconsolate dozen clustered round the placard BACK ACHE TO SAVE OUR HOSPITALS – about his solidarity with sick babies.

Driving on home for lunch, I had a strange experience.

My car stalled as I approached the London crossroads at the end of Foxglove Lane. I cursed. I twiddled the ignition key, stamped the accelerator, beat the steering wheel, while the cars behind helpfully hooted. The engine started, I moved into gear and – horror! A lorry crashed into the car ahead. But for the mysterious pause, the man climbing from the crumpled car holding his head with one hand and shaking the other fist at the lorry driver would have been me.

I did not stop – ambulance crews are wonderful, and I wanted my lunch. It occurred to me that God had been on the celestial telephone demanding in his lovable brusque way, 'Who's in charge of transport down there? Who? Oh, Jehu. Yes, of course. "For he driveth furiously" – you have my word for it. Keep a guardian eye on that doctor feller, Jehu, will you? He's playing our game.'

I mused as I later settled with my evening's Glenfiddich how prayer would be a less self-consciously awkward experience if mankind saw it as a call to his friendly neighbourhood God on a system of celestial wizardy outdoing British Telecom.

I imagined Him at His vast mahogany desk, in rough tweed suit, canary pullover and club tie, picking up the telephone.

'God here.'

'Good evening, God, this is – '

'I know who it is, of course,' he said gruffly.

'I wanted to give thanks for sparing my life this morning.'

'Glad to oblige. We never mind putting ourselves out up here for a good sort.'

'Would it be convenient to ask if any of my patients are likely to join you shortly?'

'Let's have a look. No, you've a clean sheet at the moment. Can never understand the fuss you mortals make about dying. It's the one inevitable event in your lives, and you can do bugger all about it. It's as silly to weep because you won't be alive in 100 years as that you weren't alive 100 years ago, isn't it? I put that in the mouths of a couple of French philosophers, one of whom was extremely dirty in his habits, so I expect nobody took much notice. Still, it all makes work for Mrs Huntington-Hartley. Anything else while you're on your knees?'

'I'm afraid you must get inundated with requests,' I said humbly.

'Mostly routine stuff, you know, health of the Royal Family, war and tumults, the poor and sick, My ministers of religion – and my Me! Some of them need praying for.'

I laughed.

'What's funny?' asked Sandra.

'We were having a little joke.'

She frowned. 'Who was?'

'I was talking to God.'

There was silence.

'Darling – er, that one's schizophrenia, isn't it?'

I said nothing. Much in marriage is not worth the explanation.

Mrs Gladwin was at next morning's surgery, pink spots on her cheeks.

She sat in the patients' chair and said, 'Really!'

'You've seen the vicar?' I enquired.

'Would you imagine? I'd no sooner arrived in the vicarage, naturally I was nervous, you don't usually find yourself in those sort of surroundings, when he started asking what sins I'd committed recently. The cheek!'

I pursed my lips. It seemed the equivalent of my greeting

151

someone with a polite interest in their health.

'What did you say?'

'That it's nothing to do with you,' she recounted stoutly. 'And he looked ever so stern, and said, "It's everything to do with me, sins are my job." I said, "The doctor sent me to you for my headaches, not for my sins." And he said, "Yes, but perhaps your sins are causing the headaches? And if you'll tell me them all, we can get started." '

Mrs Gladwin stopped, hands tight on lap.

'I mean, doctor,' she continued falteringly, 'I certainly wasn't going to tell him about that business with the telephone engineer you helped me over, remember, when I had to pretend I was going in for a check-up, oh, I felt ever so dreadful about it. I mean, my husband might get to know, why I wouldn't even tell Archbishop Runcie that,' she ended indignantly. 'What shall I do now, doctor?'

I automatically reached for my prescription pad. 'Have some more Valium.'

Mrs Vince was at evening surgery, giggling.

'How was the vicar?' I invited.

She said playfully, 'You meet all sorts, don't you?'

I raised my eyebrows.

'I tarted myself up a bit, I mean, you don't get invited to places like that every day, and I'd hardly got inside the door before he says, Tell me your sins. Ree-*leey*! I said.'

She laughed. I asked unhopefully what she did next.

'Oh, I could see he was after a bit of a turn-on,' she explained. 'I wasn't born yesterday. So I let him have some.'

'How did he react?'

'Couldn't have enough.'

'I suppose when you've been trained to handle sins, it was like playing tennis against a good opponent?'

'So I made a few up,' she continued enthusiastically. 'He just sat there with his mouth open saying every so often Phew. I always remember, they used to tell me at school I had a vivid imagination.'

152

I automatically reached for my prescription pad. 'Do you want some more. Valium?'

'Oh, no! I think I've kicked Valium, I really do.'

I remarked admiringly, 'That was a pretty good result from just one consultation.'

'But I'm going back, doctor,' she corrected me, grinning. 'He's lovely.'

I encountered my fellow-therapist the next Saturday morning. Bert Bullivant's protest meeting at the Town Hall against the heartless eviction of mothers and babies from Dower House was elaborated into a massive demonstration which produced a terrifying effect on the High Street traffic. I sat fuming in my car, noticing among the banners and placards waving over the packed heads LESBIAN LIB and GENTLE GAYS, who I supposed did not have much call for obstetrics and infant care.

As a policeman waved me on, I found the marchers being addressed across the official geraniums by Syd Farthingale and Bert Bullivant himself, a short fat man in a neat brown suit, large round glasses and a small moustache, with the air of an earnest schoolteacher nervously facing an unruly class. Beside him was the Rev Ron Flood, whose message I later learned was that the Government must soften its hard-nosed attitudes and keep all National Health hospitals open even if there were no patients for them. I felt charitably that he was not alone among modern turbulent priests in circulating only hot air.

I was surprised that evening when he arrived at my house looking as full of sins as a Christmas pudding of currants.

'Perhaps, doctor, your profession is more difficult than it seems,' he began awkwardly, accepting an Old Fettercairn.

'Oh, I agree absolutely.'

'I have been searching my conscience all week why I managed to upset little Mrs Gladwin.'

'I think she's a bit touchy about her sins.'

'But I was only trying to relieve her inner tensions by inviting open discussion of her guilt.' He leant forward earnestly. 'Freud would surely have done the same, had he been vicar of St Alphege's?'

I agreed wholeheartedly.

'I studied psychology seriously in theological college, you know. But I cannot for the life of me see any reason for Mrs Gladwin hitting me over the head with a flower vase.'

I expressed the wish that the injury was superficial.

'I've still got the lump. But Mrs Vince –' He stopped. 'She has no such inhibitions.'

He stared at his toes in his sandals. 'She could tell a young clergyman a lot of things he'd never learned in theological college.'

'She could probably tell a young doctor a lot of things he'd never learned in medical school,' I concurred generously.

'She suggested I performed the laying-on of hands with her headache. 'Nothing wrong with that?'

He drew a deep breath. 'At her next visit, which happened to be the next day, I suggested when we were well into her sins that we took a tea break. She said, Oh, lovely. I went to my kitchen and brewed up. I brought the pot in and dropped the tray. She was sitting what they call topless.'

'That's a pretty puny sin,' I objected. 'Broken beer bottles on the beach are far more dangerous.'

'Yes, but she wanted the laying-on of hands with her palpitations. Not the sort of thing a clergyman can allow himself to do.'

'I have to agree,' I commiserated.

'I think I should abandon the medical ministry, doctor.'

'I couldn't agree with you more.' I rose. 'Sorry I can't offer you another whisky, but there's the phone, and I'm on call.'

It was Jim Whynn. He felt fine, but could I come on Sunday morning to check up?

I arrived at breakfast time. He was pacing the circular living room in a fury.

'Look at that!'

He stuck his finger towards the newspaper which had disrupted both our lives.

'Lord Churchford? Yes, I saw he was on the front page,' I remarked.

'He's no right to be. He ought to be dead. I thought he was dead for years. How old is he? Ninety-nine? A hundred and twenty? He could have walked off with the first prize at that senile shindig of the *Echo's*.'

'I thought he was dead, too. He's a patient. Haven't seen him for five years. He'd sprained a wrist chopping down trees. He must be as tough as treacle toffee.'

Jim snatched up the paper and glared at Lord Churchford's photograph, resembling a walrus discovered after several centuries in peat.

Lord Churchford's attack on the closure of Dower House was ferocious, feline and formidable. The Government had forgotten that Nye Bevan – a personal friend, charming chap, much misunderstood, it was perfectly disgraceful he got kicked down the front steps of White's Club in St James's for describing the Tories as lower than vermin in 1948 – accepted Dower House as a much appreciated loan to the newborn National Health Service. Dower House was as sturdily independent as other hospitals catering specially for Catholics, Masons, trade unionists and women.

'This argument watertight?' Jim asked impatiently.

I nodded. 'Oh, yes. They were queer fish which Nye Bevan was happy to let escape the national net. Dower House is no more part of the NHS than the Ritz Hotel.'

Jim groaned. 'Unfortunately, old Churchford's become a venerable national figure, after years of being our craftiest politician since the days when they risked ending up in two pieces on Tower Hill. Nothing is more embarrassing to the Government than the plaintive mooing of sacred cows.'

Jim read the story again. 'He could have as easily made his point in a letter to me, but he's luxuriating in his lifelong habit of making as much mischief as possible. How delight-fully irresponsible are childhood and senility! If he carried out this threat to mobilize his noble friends once Parliament reassembles, he could badly hurt the Government – if not

155

defeat us.' He complained crossly, 'I do wish the House of Lords would realize it's only a legislative Madame Tussaud's.'

He tossed the paper aside. 'I suppose we can't close down a hospital we don't own,' he admitted. 'But there must be a way round it. There's a way round everything. God knows how the mistake arose, but I'll see the civil servant responsible is posted tomorrow to Northern Ireland.'

An antidote had been crystallizing in my mind.

'Do you think it would help, Jim, if I – as a senior Churchford GP – told the *Echo* that closing Dower House was an inspired act of clinical slum clearance? It would be no trouble. I'm playing golf with Arthur Crevin this afternoon. The Fleet Street papers are sure to take it up.'

Jim stroked his chin.

'Yes, I think that's a sound plan. I could attach some remarks of my own, perhaps a word from the Minister. I *must* keep this bandwagon on the road, even if the wheels seem to have dropped off. Thank you, Richard, go ahead,' he said thoughtfully, adding with a quick look, 'I haven't forgotten my promise of a job on the new committee.'

'That's nothing to do with it,' I told him firmly. 'I'll say publicly that Dower House should be shut only because I think that's the best medicine for Churchford.' I decided to rattle another iron in his newly-fanned fire of gratitude. 'Annabel Blackadder – '

'Oh, her,' he said unenthusiastically. 'If you've got the wretched girl so much at heart, I'll see if I can find her something. Possibly one of my opponents might think it a useful political point to employ her as a research assistant. Bertie Bullivant might bite,' he speculated.

Driving home, I had a strange experience.

One of the thunderstorms which had been threatening to overwhelm Saturday's demonstration broke upon Churchford. A cat streaked through the pounding rain, I braked, skidded, hit a lamppost.

I was shaken, the car dented, the lamppost leaning. I saw

156

endless trouble with garages, insurance claims, the police. I gingerly continued my journey, thinking of God on the heavenly blower. 'That Jethro? Joash? Whatsisname? Jehu! That's it. The doctor chappie's letting the side down. He's playing politics. Give him a taste of the frighteners.'

21

'Good news,' I informed Mrs Jenkins, arriving for morning surgery in the middle of the following week. 'I've found that assistant you've. been hankering for all summer.'

'That's a relief,' she exclaimed. 'I hope she's suitable?'

'Eminently. Just turned twenty, pretty, lively, eager to start a useful job and admirably adapted to strict discipline.'

Mrs Jenkins tapped her lips speculatively with the butt of her ballpoint.

'Annabel Blackadder,' I unveiled.

'Oh! Well.'

'Why look so doubtful? She might instead have the fashionable post of assistant to some MP, except that she can't type and hates using the telephone.'

'What's the girl going to do here, if she can't type?' Mrs Jenkins asked reasonably.

'I thought she might look after the patients' files.'

'That would be a relief, I must say.' She hesitated. 'I suppose she's reliable?'

'You mean honest, don't you?'

'I suppose I do.'

'If you'd suffered like her for a moment's silly impulse, wouldn't it make you as honest as George Washington?'

She changed the subject. 'You seem to be in the news again.'

That morning's *Churchford Echo* zestfully reported on the front page my swim against the tide of public opinion.

'It's a modest contribution to the reduction of infant mortality,' I told her. 'The Dower House drains are well-known to have killed off several dowagers.'

My first patient was the vicar. He was suffering from anxiety, headaches and palpitations.

'My experience in trying to assist you, doctor, was surprisingly upsetting,' he revealed, shifting nervously in the patients' chair. 'I've suddenly felt my parochial work's getting on top of me. Particularly,' he broke off, 'with my involvement in this disgusting decision to shut a hospital – which I see you're in favour of.'

'Both politicians and their voters are obsessed with hospitals,' I told him airily. 'Which make the population no more healthy than churches make them religious.'

'Last night I felt at the end of my tether,' he confessed gloomily. 'Living alone in that Victorian vicarage can make a man feel suicidal, you know. Having no one to pour out my troubles to. So I thought I'd best come and see you, doctor. I expect that's what a lot of your patients decide? There seems to be no one else.'

I automatically reached for my prescription pad.

'The National Formulary,' I said comfortingly, 'like the Holy Scripture, containeth all things necessary for salvation.'

I wrote a prescription for Valium.

An idea struck me.

'If you're short of a sympathetic ear – day or night – telephone the Samaritans. Ask for Mrs Osgood. I can guarantee hers.'

He thanked me warmly. I felt I had to get him in peak form for the wedding on Saturday week.

At the golf club that evening I met Dr Quaggy.

'Richard, you and I are very old friends,' he insisted, wedging me into a corner of the bar with his gin-and-tonic. 'And I should be failing in a friend's first duty did I not tell you the distress of all we medical people in Churchford at your backing this perfectly heartless Government decision to close Dower House. I gather Lord Churchford was quite apoplectic when he saw this morning's *Echo*. That's how I became aware of your opinions, as it happens,' he revealed. 'His Lordship was on the telephone at breakfast time, asking me to take him over as a private patient. I hope you don't mind?'

159

'Not at all,' I told him generously.

Who did he remind me of? It was passing from the puzzling to the infuriating.

'I don't see why I should have *all* the distinguished patients in Churchford,' I conceded.

'Naturally, we understand you feel an obligation to Jim Whynn after landing him in such trouble,' Dr Quaggy continued gently. 'And there is of course this excellent job he's offered you on the Government committee investigating the rest of us GPs.'

'How did you hear of that?' I asked crossly.

'Oh, it's all round Churchford,' he informed me amiably. 'I believe the news originated from Mrs Whynn. She seemed to think that your being in so powerful a position might increase our enthusiasm to see her on the Family Practice Committee. I suppose she was implying vaguely that pressure could always be put on you via her husband.'

'There is no truth whatever in my joining any government committee.' I was so furious I splashed my Glenlivet. 'I have made up my mind firmly and finally against it.'

'What a pity,' he lamented softly. 'We all thought it an admirable occupation for your retirement.'

'Nor is there any truth that I am bloody retiring!'

'I'm sure we'll all be delighted to hear that, when last April it seemed the only course open to you,' he told me sympathetically.

I drove home. I telephoned the oast house. The Norland nurse said that Mr and Mrs Whynn were away until the weekend.

I strode into the back garden. I angrily paced the lawn. I heard the vicar calling through the twilight. He said he had forgotten to mention the shakes as well. He showed me over the hedge. I told him to double the dose. Darkness drove me into the house. Sandra burst out that I seemed to be taking no interest in my daughter's wedding. I told her I had so many troubles I should have taken no interest in my own. She became cross, and left me alone by bottling jam.

160

I poured myself a Talisker and stared at the wall. I shot up in my armchair. Suddenly I remembered who Quaggy reminded me of.

No!

Impossible.

Incredible.

Belinda's clever Kevin.

Unbelievable!

Or was it?

Human sexual behaviour was as freakishly unpredictable as a madman's. Freud made a reputation from it.

I slapped my thigh and roared with laughter. Sandra came in and asked if I was enjoying another joke with God.

Friday morning's paper announced that the Government had collapsed.

Dower House hospital was staying open. Mothers and babies were as close to the Cabinet's heart as to Syd Farthingale's. I felt like Dr Lonelyhearts at the end of his marathon.

I arrived at the surgery to find the waiting room tighter crammed than in the bronchitic months of midwinter.

'What's up?' I demanded, striding into Mrs Jenkins' small office. 'What do all those patients want?'

Pink and flustered, she said, 'To change their doctor.'

I was shocked. 'Am I that bad? Have I perpetrated some disastrous stroke of mass malpractice overnight?'

'It's not you,' she explained. 'It's her.'

Sitting expressionless at the receptionist's desk was Annabel.

'But she's only been here a couple of days,' I exclaimed. 'What's she done?'

'The patients are all frightened their medical records will appear in the newspapers.'

I beat my brow with my fists.

'People,' I complained, 'can be horribly beastly.' I commanded, 'Annabel. Come here.'

I put my arm around her. I took her into the waiting room.

161

'Good morning,' I addressed them. 'I gather some of you wish to change your doctor?'

There were shifty exchanges of glances, embarrassed muttering, some whispering, 'That's her.'

'Would you change your minds and remain my patients if I myself changed my new assistant here?' I invited.

Muttering and nodding. Unmistakable indications of assent all round.

I told them, 'As I have no intention of losing a valuable employee whom I trust utterly, and as you seem to have no confidence in my judgement of people, so you cannot have much in my abilities as a doctor, I should be delighted for us to part company. Please queue up to see Mrs Jenkins. I recommend you join Dr Quaggy.'

I marched into my consulting room rubbing my hands briskly. I felt I had already done one good day's work.

Mrs Gladwin was already in the patients' chair. I automatically reached for my prescription pad.

'But I think I can cut down on the capsules, doctor,' she announced.

'Good! Not feeling so tense? No headaches? Palpitations gone?'

'Yes, I'm ever so much better,' she agreed cheerfully. 'Perhaps it was the vicar after all? I mean, letting loose at him like that. Do you know, doctor, I felt that a big, tight spring had suddenly come apart, whanggg, inside me.'

I observed, 'Many therapists favour the transference of the patients' inner aggression to the psychiatrist. Though not commonly by means of a flower vase.'

She looked shameful. 'I'm ever so sorry about the vase, doctor. I do not know what came over me. I've been meaning to apologize to the vicar, as I see him every day, sometimes I think I'm looking at him all day long.'

I was puzzled.

'You know I work in my husband's office, doctor? It's in the High Street, opposite the Dingley Dell. All week he's been sitting there drinking cup after cup of coffee. I've no

162

idea why he's suddenly got so fond of it.'

'Caffeine poisoning!' I clasped my brow. 'That would account for his symptoms, including the shakes.'

'I beg your pardon, doctor?'

'I expect he just wants to keep alert while he's praying for us all. The vicar is very conscientious.'

I could hear God on the divine intercom, chortling, 'Good show, Luke! You fixed that dim doctor nicely, didn't you?'

I appeared at the oast house in early evening. The couple had just arrived from London. Jim seemed elated. He took me into the circular living room and poured me a Highland Park.

'I should have imagined,' I observed soberly, 'that the Government had so much egg on its face that it needs only a couple of crossed anchovies to turn it into a Scotch woodcock.'

'You mean keeping Dower House as a going concern?' He poured himself a large gin. 'But we were intending to do that all along.'

'It's not what you told me,' I reminded him indignantly.

'My dear Richard! However friendly we might be, I cannot share Government secrets with you, surely?' he told me blandly. 'Besides, I imagined a man of your sharp intelligence would have seen through my little plan.'

'That's very flattering. But a good sort, even of the highest intelligence, does not exert it to sniff out suspiciously the deceits of his friends.' I drew myself up and added cuttingly, 'Nor does he need to.'

'Richard! You're annoyed,' he told me mildly. 'Really, you've no need. These sorts of strategems are everyday commerce in politics. If you were a professional politician, you'd think no more of them than the aches and pains you handle as a professional doctor.'

'Of course I'm annoyed,' I insisted. 'For saying publicly that pesthouse deserved shutting down, if not burning down, I've been vilified by the medical community and probably the entire citizenry of Churchford. Not to mention Lord

Churchford. And God knows what Lesbian Lib and Gentle Gays think of me. Now I'm seen as a misguided fool, because it's staying open anyway.'

'When I explain what the plan was, I'm sure you'll be as delighted with the outcome as I am. Didn't you notice a small item about Churchford's General Hospital in this morning's papers?'

I shook my head.

'Which just shows how effectively the scheme worked. You know the National Health Service is sitting on 200 million quids' worth of empty property? Nurses' homes with rooms fit for Victorian scullery maids, doctors' quarters slipping from the uncomfortable to the uninhabitable, disused wards, abandoned laundries, condemned kitchens, crumbling back yards, tottering out-houses? Why, the hospitals were richer in land than the monasteries when Nye Bevan did a Henry VIII and dissolved them 310 years later. Henry VIII sensibly sold it off to cut taxes at a stroke. So should we. But everyone objects. ACHE complains that nurses already on poverty pay will be thrown on the streets, probably to make their living there.' He shrugged hopelessly. 'Henry VIII had it easy, he simply burnt alive anyone who disagreed with his book-keeping. We must substitute a smokescreen for combustion. So I concocted the fuss over Dower House to divert attention while the Department of Health quietly sold off the General's rotting buildings,' he revealed complacently.

I asked blankly, 'Who to?'

'We had an offer we couldn't refuse from an American company shortly to erect a splendid private hospital on the site. Just what Churchford lacks – I said as much, you may remember, when you insisted on my seeing that dreadful psychiatrist back in the spring. The Americans are so pleased, they're calling it the Whynn Clinic. I'll be laying the foundation-stone before Christmas. Having a hospital named after you in your political base would probably keep you secure even if red revolution broke out. I'm afraid all this

164

is going to upset Bertie Bullivant dreadfully.'

I exclaimed, 'Dower House stays open because it was going to, anyway? So he really got nothing at all for giving in to that new motorway through the workers' semis?'

Jim sighed. 'Not really. Particularly as that old fool Lord Churchford gave us a wonderful excuse for climbing down as defenders of his constitutional rights. I really must send the old orang-utang a case of Croft's best port. You see, Richard, politics is the art of the possible – meaning whatever you can possibly get away with.'

A burning political question remained unanswered.

'What's in it for you?' I demanded.

Jim Whynn beamed. 'You're looking at the next Minister of State at the Department of Transport. It's been promised in the forthcoming reshuffle. A wonderful end to the whole Dower House affair.'

'Jim,' I told him, 'you leave me with only two points to make. One, I do not wish for this committee job you offered.'

'Oh, I meant to tell you,' he mentioned. 'It's fallen through. Old Forditch at the Ministry is being given his peerage and sent to one of these enormously lucrative jobs with the EEC in Brussels. He's looking forward to it tremendously. He can't stand his wife, and he'll be able to have lots of mistresses. I believe they all do.'

'Secondly, I'm delighted that your political career has flourished despite the blight which nipped it in the spring. I am only sorry that you have used me as the manure. I can no longer feel comfortable having you as a patient. I recommend you join Dr Quaggy. Good evening.'

He was saying in amazment, 'Richard! You *are* being dreadfully touchy.' But I had slammed the door.

I called on my way home at the vicarage. My day's work could not end before I had cured a case of caffeine poisoning. I seemed to remember it could lead to convulsions and hallucinations, embarrassing in the clergyman officiating at my daughter's wedding.

The door was opened by Mrs Osgood.

165

'Why, doctor, how lovely to see you again!' she greeted me huskily. 'I'm so glad you suggested Ron phoned me at the Samaritans. Now I shall be able to give him my personal attention. He's just making a pot of tea,' she informed me, dropping her eyes. 'Shall I get him?'

'Don't worry,' I told her. 'I'm sure what he's suffering from will shortly be cured. Good evening.'

22

It was Saturday week. The marquee was up on the lawn. The weather was wonderful.

I was dressing myself to resemble a Victorian consultant physician. My daughter was magnificent in flowing white. The house was in turmoil. Sandra announced that Mrs Whynn was downstairs and had to see me urgently.

'Impossible,' I said testily. 'Jilly and I leave for the church in half an hour.'

'I told her. But she won't go away.'

I slipped on my frock coat hired from The Perfect Gent in the High Street and went down to the living room.

'Glass of champagne?' I offered Charlotte.

'No thank you, Richard.' She stood by the window, looking subdued. 'I know it couldn't be a more inconvenient moment to call.'

'You've been turned down by Dr Quaggy?'

'We're not going to Dr Quaggy. If you'll be charitable and have us.'

I shrugged.

'You've suffered dreadfully in Jim's hands,' she continued solemnly. 'I hope you didn't think I condoned all he did? Or worse, didn't notice it? I wanted to make you a little happier for your daughter's wedding by saying how sorry I am.'

I was touched.

'Jim was only playing his game,' I conceded. 'I wasn't playing at all. Politicians are too dangerous for a simpleton like me. I thought I could handle Jim, as I handled difficult patients. Sandra warned me that I couldn't. It was vanity, which inspires women but ruins men.'

'You should never have let Jim go near a psychiatrist.'

I justified myself, 'He *did* say he was contemplating suicide.'

'Oh, Jim isn't the suicidal type at all. I don't think any MPs are.' She smiled. 'Who would destroy what they are most fond of, themselves? He said it only to make sure you'd send him to one. He knew perfectly well that dreadful girl in Soho had recognized him, and wanted some insurance in case it got into the papers.'

I noticed the arrival of the beribboned white Rolls-Royce which Sandra had insisted should drive Jilly and myself round the corner to St Alphege's.

'At least he told *you* all about her,' I reflected.

'Oh, heavens, that girl wasn't the only one! All his life, Jim's been running through women like a harvester in a hayfield. He's dreadfully attractive, of course. And MPs fascinate women as men of power but accessible, sometimes pressingly so. I've threatened to divorce him more than once, but he's talked me out of it. You can't be too cautious in a stuffy place like Churchford. So I've looked away. He's persuaded me that his career comes before everything. Perhaps I'm as simple as you, Richard? I think the bride's ready to leave.'

But she was not. A police car had stopped at the front gate. An inspector was on the doorstep.

'Very sorry to intrude at this moment, Dr Gordon,' he apologized gravely. 'But of course, we didn't know it was a joyous occasion this afternoon.'

'What's the matter?' I asked impatiently. 'Not the lamppost, surely? I offered to pay for a new one.'

'We have Miss Annabel Blackadder at the station, and she gave your name as her employer. She was arrested after one of my officers had noticed her unlocking the front door of your surgery when it was empty on a Saturday afternoon. She came out carrying the contents of your drug cupboard in a couple of plastic bags.'

I beat my brow with my fists.

'Will you look into the station, doctor?'

168

'Just as soon as my daughter has been pronounced man and wife.'

'There's no hurry. We're not letting her go on bail. Not this time.'

My son Andy, arrived from Baltimore that morning and also dressed like a Victorian physician, burst from the front door.

'Dad! It's Sir Damian Havers on the phone. He says he's dying.'

'Then tell him to carry on,' I replied. 'Jilly, my dear, it is time for me to give you to Peter.'

In the car I held Jilly's hand and said, 'I'm afraid I haven't given the attention I should to the happiest day of your life. But I've had a lot of things on my plate. Mostly, highly unpalatable.'

'Poor daddy.' She smiled through her veil.

'I have been made into Churchford's prize fool. "Doctors, priests, magistrates, and officers know men as thoroughly as if they had made them",' I repeated. 'I'm sorry to quote Jean-Paul Sartre on the way to your wedding, dear, but the bloody man got it wrong.'

'Don't worry, daddy.' She squeezed my hand tightly. 'You're a good sort. The whole world knows it.'

We arrived at St Alphege's. I do not respond to ceremonies – religious, royal or judicial. I never find them more significant than everyone dressing up for the golf club fancy dress ball. Perhaps I am a puritan, robed only in my glorious prejudices? Perhaps I am too vain for self-abasement before powers mightier and more mysterious than mankind? Or perhaps a lifetime of medical practice has sadly left me without illusions?

We entered the church. I reflected that I should have no option about participation in my next ceremony there, which would be my funeral.

Jilly had brought me great comfort on her wedding day. She said everyone thought me a good sort. And in my heart I believed they were correct. Except, of course, for the occasional touch of *Torschlusspanik!*

169